101+

Delicious

DIABETIC

RECIPES

The Ultimate Fuss-Free Cookbook

PUBLICATIONS INTERNATIONAL, LTD.

Nutritional Analysis: Linda R. Yoakam, M.S., R.D.

Photography: Sanders Studios, Inc., Chicago
Photographers: Kathy Sanders, Kathy Watt
Studio Coordinator: Kathy Ores
Prop Stylist: Patty Higgins
Food Stylists: Mary-Helen Steindler, Donna Coates
Assistant Food Stylist: Corrine Kozlak

Pictured on the front cover: Chocolate-Berry Cheesecake *(page 74)*.
Pictured on the back cover *(clockwise from top left):* Apple Slaw with Poppy Seed Dressing *(page 24),* Cashew Chicken *(page 38)* and Chicken Fajitas with Cowpoke Barbecue Sauce *(page 54)*.

ISBN: 0-7853-1381-8

Manufactured in U.S.A.

8 7 6 5 4 3 2 1

Microwave Cooking: Microwave ovens vary in wattage. The microwave cooking times given in this publication are approximate. Use the cooking times as guidelines and check for doneness before adding more time. Consult manufacturer's instructions for suitable microwave-safe cooking dishes.

101+
Delicious DIABETIC RECIPES

The Ultimate Fuss-Free Cookbook

Facts About Diabetes

Low calorie, low fat, low cholesterol and low sodium—buzzwords of the decade and for a good reason. People today are more aware than ever before of the roles that diet and exercise play in maintaining a healthful lifestyle. For people with diabetes and their families, the positive impact good nutrition and physical activity have on well being is very familiar. Diabetes is a disease that affects the body's ability to utilize glucose as a source of fuel. When glucose is improperly utilized, it can build up in the bloodstream creating higher than normal blood sugar levels. Left unchecked, elevated blood sugar levels may lead to the development of more serious long-term complications like blindness and heart and kidney disease.

Not all cases of diabetes are alike. In fact, the disease presents itself in two very distinct forms—Type I and Type II. Development of diabetes during childhood or adolescence is typical of Type I or juvenile-onset diabetes. These individuals are unable to make insulin, a hormone produced by the pancreas that moves glucose from the bloodstream into the body's cells where it is used as a source of fuel. Daily injections of insulin, coupled with a balanced meal plan, are the focus of treatment. Insulin is usually produced in those individuals diagnosed with Type II diabetes, the more common form of the disease, but the amount is insufficient to meet the body's needs. Treatment includes balanced eating, moderate weight loss, exercise and, in extreme cases, oral hypoglycemic agents or insulin injections.

MAXIMIZE HEALTH, MINIMIZE COMPLICATIONS

Diabetes increases one's risk of developing high blood pressure and high blood cholesterol levels. Over time, elevated levels may progress to more serious complications, including heart disease, stroke, kidney disease and hypertension. Research shows that individuals with diabetes are nineteen times more likely to develop kidney disease and four times more likely to suffer from heart disease or a stroke than people who do not have diabetes. While heredity plays a major role in the development of these complications, regular check-ups with your physician and registered dietitian to fine tune treatment strategies are good ways to help minimize complications. Strategies for treatment vary among individuals, yet overall goals remain the same: achieving and maintaining near-normal blood sugar levels by balancing food intake, insulin and activity, achieving optimal blood cholesterol levels, and improving overall health through good nutrition.

BALANCE IS THE KEY

Achieving optimal nutrition often requires lifestyle changes to balance the intake of nutrients. The United States Department of Agriculture and the United States Department of Health and Human Services developed the Dietary Guidelines to simplify the basics of balanced eating and to help all individuals develop a healthful eating plan. Several of the guidelines follow but were adjusted to include the revised 1994 American Diabetes Association's Nutrition Recommendations. Because recommendations are broad, work with your physician and registered dietitian to individualize the guidelines to meet your specific needs.

Eat a variety of foods. Energy, protein, vitamins, minerals and fiber are essential for optimal health, but no one food contains them all. Including a wide range of foods in your diet and using fats and oils sparingly throughout the day are easy ways to consume all the nutrients your body needs. Carbohydrate should comprise between 45 and 55 percent of total calories and protein should contribute between 10 and 20 percent.

Maintain a healthy weight. Excess weight can worsen your diabetes and encourages the development of more severe complications. Research shows that shedding 10 to 20 pounds is enough to initiate positive results. Combining a healthful eating plan with physical activity outlined by your health care team is the best medicine for maintaining a healthy weight.

Choose a diet low in fat, saturated fat and cholesterol. Fat has more than double the calories of an equal amount of protein or carbohydrates. Thus, diets low in fat make it easier to maintain a desirable weight and decrease the likelihood of developing high blood cholesterol levels. Limit fat to no more than 30 percent of total calories, saturated fat to no more than 10 percent of total calories from fat and daily cholesterol to no more than 600 mg. The 30 percent of calories from fat goal applies to a total diet over time, not to a single food, serving of a recipe or meal.

Choose a diet with plenty of vegetables, fruits and grain products. Vitamins, minerals, fiber and complex carbohydrates abound in these low fat food choices. Filling up on fiber leaves less room for fat and may produce a slight decrease in blood cholesterol levels. Antioxidants such as beta carotene and the vitamins C and E may protect against heart disease, while magnesium, phosphorous and calcium are minerals that may keep blood pressure levels under control.

Use sugars in moderation. The ban on sugar has been lifted for people with diabetes but it is not altogether gone. The new guidelines for simple sugar intake are based on scientific research that indicates that carbohydrate in the form of simple sugars *does not* raise blood sugar levels more rapidly than any other type of carbohydrate food. What is more important is the *total amount* of carbohydrate consumed, not the source. However, keep in mind that since simple sugars are loaded with calories, contain no vitamins and minerals, and are linked to the development of cavities, it is still a good idea to limit your intake of simple sugars to no more than 25 percent of total carbohydrate.

Use salt and sodium in moderation. Some people with diabetes may be more sensitive to sodium than others making them more susceptible to high blood pressure. Minimize this risk by limiting sodium intake to no more than 2,400 mg a day (about 1 teaspoon of salt) and choosing single food items with less than 400 mg of sodium and entrées with less than 800 mg of sodium per serving.

FACTS ABOUT THE FOOD

The recipes in this publication were designed with people with diabetes in mind. But all are based on the principles of sound nutrition as outlined by the Dietary Guidelines making them perfect for the entire family. Though the recipes in this publication are not intended as a medically therapeutic program, nor as a substitute for medically approved meal plans for individuals with diabetes, they are low in calories, fat, sodium and cholesterol and will fit easily into an individualized meal plan designed by your physician, registered dietitian and you.

The nutrition information that appears with each recipe was calculated by an independent nutrition consulting firm and The Dietary Exchanges are based on the Exchange Lists for Meal Planning developed by American Diabetes Association/the American Dietetic Association. Every effort has been made to check the accuracy of these numbers. However, because numerous variables account for a wide range of values in certain foods, all analyses that appear in this book should be considered approximate.

- The analysis of each recipe includes all the ingredients that are listed in that recipe, except ingredients labeled as "optional" or "for garnish."

- If a range is offered for an ingredient, the first amount given was used to calculate the nutrition information.

- If an ingredient is presented with an option ("2 cups hot, cooked rice or noodles" for example), the first item listed was used to calculate the nutritional information.

- Foods shown in photographs on the same serving plate and offered as "serve with" suggestions at the end of a recipe are not included in the recipe analysis unless they are listed in the ingredient list.

- Meat should be trimmed of all visible fat since this is reflected in the nutritional analysis.

- In recipes calling for cooked rice or noodles, the analysis was based on rice or noodles that were prepared without added salt and fat.

- Most processed foods contain a significant amount of sodium and the amount of sodium is reflected in the analysis. Rinsing canned or jarred processed foods such as beans and tuna under cold running water for one minute eliminates between 40 and 60 percent of added sodium.

Sandwiches & Snacks

Add flair to midday munching with this delicious collection of sandwiches and snacks. Brown-baggers will welcome the outstanding selection of take-a-long treats.

Black Bean Tostadas

- 1 cup rinsed, drained canned black beans, mashed
- 2 teaspoons chili powder
  Nonstick cooking spray
- 4 (8-inch) corn tortillas
- 1 cup washed, torn romaine lettuce leaves
- 1 cup chopped seeded tomato
- ½ cup chopped onion
- ½ cup plain nonfat yogurt
- 2 jalapeño peppers, seeded, finely chopped*

*Jalapeño peppers can sting and irritate the skin. Wear rubber gloves when handling peppers and do not touch eyes.

1. Combine beans and chili powder in small saucepan. Cook 5 minutes over medium heat or until heated through, stirring occasionally.

2. Spray large nonstick skillet with cooking spray. Heat over medium heat until hot. Sprinkle tortillas with water; place tortillas in skillet, one at a time. Cook 20 to 30 seconds or until tortillas are hot and pliable, turning once.

3. Spread bean mixture evenly over tortillas. Layer lettuce, tomato, onion, yogurt and peppers evenly over bean mixture. Garnish as desired. Serve immediately.

Makes 4 servings

Dietary Exchanges per Serving:
1½ Starch/Bread, 1½ Vegetable

NUTRIENTS PER SERVING:

Calories	146
% calories from fat	9
Total Fat	2 g
Saturated Fat	<1 g
Cholesterol	1 mg
Sodium	466 mg
Carbohydrate	29 g
Dietary Fiber	5 g
Protein	9 g
Calcium	119 mg
Iron	2 mg
Vitamin A	129 RE
Vitamin C	18 mg

Black Bean Tostada

Meatless Sloppy Joe

Meatless Sloppy Joes

    Nonstick cooking spray
2 **cups thinly sliced onions**
2 **cups chopped green bell peppers**
2 **cloves garlic, finely chopped**
2 **tablespoons ketchup**
1 **tablespoon prepared mustard**
1 **can (about 15 ounces) kidney beans,
    rinsed, drained and mashed**
1 **can (8 ounces) tomato sauce**
1 **teaspoon chili powder**
    Cider vinegar
2 **sandwich rolls, halved**

1. Spray large nonstick skillet with cooking spray. Heat over medium-high heat until hot. Add onions, peppers and garlic. Cook and stir 5 minutes or until vegetables are tender. Stir in ketchup and mustard.

2. Add beans, tomato sauce and chili powder to skillet. Reduce heat to medium-low. Cook and stir 5 minutes or until thickened, adding up to ⅓ cup cider vinegar if mixture is too dry.

3. Spoon bean mixture evenly over sandwich roll halves. Garnish as desired.

Makes 4 servings

Dietary Exchanges per Serving:
2 Starch/Bread, 3 Vegetable, ½ Fat

NUTRIENTS PER SERVING:

Calories	242
% calories from fat	7
Total Fat	2 g
Saturated Fat	<1 g
Cholesterol	0 mg
Sodium	994 mg
Carbohydrate	48 g
Dietary Fiber	10 g
Protein	10 g
Calcium	102 mg
Iron	3 mg
Vitamin A	158 RE
Vitamin C	113 mg

Hummus

1 can (about 15 ounces) garbanzo
    beans (chick-peas), rinsed and
    drained
3 tablespoons lemon juice
4½ teaspoons tahini*
½ teaspoon ground cumin
¼ teaspoon salt
¼ teaspoon ground black pepper
½ cup chopped tomato
⅓ cup chopped red onion
⅓ cup chopped celery
⅓ cup chopped seeded cucumber
⅓ cup chopped green or red bell pepper
2 whole pita breads

*Tahini, a thick paste made from ground sesame seeds, is available in the ethnic section of major supermarkets, Middle Eastern markets or health food stores.

1. In food processor or blender combine beans, lemon juice, tahini, cumin, salt and black pepper; process until smooth. If mixture is too thick to spread, add water until desired consistency is reached.

2. Spoon bean mixture into serving bowl. Top with tomato, onion, celery, cucumber and bell pepper.

3. Preheat broiler. Split pita breads horizontally in half to form 4 rounds. Stack rounds; cut into sixths to form 24 wedges. Place wedges on baking sheet. Broil 3 minutes or until crisp.

4. Serve Hummus with warm pita bread wedges. *Makes 6 servings*

Dietary Exchanges per Serving:
2 Starch/Bread, ½ Vegetable, ½ Fat

NUTRIENTS PER SERVING:
6 pita bread wedges, ½ cup Hummus

Calories	188
% calories from fat	17
Total Fat	4 g
Saturated Fat	1 g
Cholesterol	0 mg
Sodium	542 mg
Carbohydrate	33 g
Dietary Fiber	4 g
Protein	7 g
Calcium	69 mg
Iron	3 mg
Vitamin A	24 RE
Vitamin C	23 mg

California Rolls

1 cup reduced fat ricotta cheese
2 (11-inch) flour tortillas
1 tomato, thinly sliced
2 cups washed, torn spinach or lettuce
    leaves
1 cup chopped onion
½ teaspoon dried oregano leaves
½ teaspoon dried basil leaves
1 cup alfalfa sprouts
4 ounces thinly sliced turkey breast

1. Spread ½ cup of cheese evenly over each tortilla to within ¼ inch of edge. Starting 1 inch from bottom edges, layer tomato, spinach, onion, oregano, basil, alfalfa sprouts and turkey evenly over two-thirds of tortillas.

2. Starting from bottom, roll up tortillas jelly-roll style. Wrap in plastic wrap; refrigerate 1 hour. Unwrap; cut crosswise into 10 (1-inch) slices. *Makes 20 slices*

Dietary Exchanges per Serving:
1½ Starch/Bread, 1½ Lean Meat, 1 Vegetable

NUTRIENTS PER SERVING:
5 slices

Calories	209
% calories from fat	17
Total Fat	4 g
Saturated Fat	<1 g
Cholesterol	28 mg
Sodium	233 mg
Carbohydrate	28 g
Dietary Fiber	2 g
Protein	16 g
Calcium	132 mg
Iron	3 mg
Vitamin A	233 RE
Vitamin C	17 mg

Italian Meatball Subs

Nonstick cooking spray
½ cup chopped onion
3 teaspoons finely chopped garlic, divided
1 can (14½ ounces) Italian-style crushed tomatoes, undrained
2 bay leaves
2½ teaspoons dried basil leaves, divided
2 teaspoons dried oregano leaves, divided
¾ teaspoon ground black pepper, divided
¼ teaspoon crushed red pepper
½ pound lean ground beef
⅓ cup chopped green onions
⅓ cup bread crumbs
¼ cup chopped fresh parsley
1 egg white
½ teaspoon dried marjoram leaves
½ teaspoon ground mustard
4 French bread rolls, warmed, halved

1. Spray large nonstick saucepan with cooking spray. Heat over medium heat until hot. Add onion and 2 teaspoons garlic. Cook and stir 5 minutes or until onion is tender. Add tomatoes with liquid, bay leaves, 2 teaspoons basil, 1 teaspoon oregano, ½ teaspoon black pepper and red pepper; cover. Simmer 30 minutes, stirring occasionally. Remove and discard bay leaves.

2. Combine meat, green onions, bread crumbs, parsley, egg white, 2 tablespoons water, remaining 1 teaspoon garlic, remaining ½ teaspoon basil, remaining 1 teaspoon oregano, remaining ¼ teaspoon black pepper, marjoram and mustard in medium bowl until well blended. Shape into 16 small meatballs.

3. Spray large nonstick skillet with cooking spray. Heat over medium heat until hot. Add meatballs. Cook 5 minutes or until meatballs are no longer pink in center, turning occasionally.

4. Add meatballs to tomato sauce. Cook 5 minutes, stirring occasionally.

5. Place 4 meatballs in each roll. Spoon additional sauce over meatballs. Serve immediately. *Makes 4 servings*

Dietary Exchanges per Serving:
2 Starch/Bread, 2 Lean Meat, 1 Vegetable

NUTRIENTS PER SERVING:

Calories	282
% calories from fat	30
Total Fat	9 g
Saturated Fat	3 g
Cholesterol	35 mg
Sodium	497 mg
Carbohydrate	32 g
Dietary Fiber	1 g
Protein	18 g
Calcium	134 mg
Iron	4 mg
Vitamin A	142 RE
Vitamin C	29 mg

Cook's Tip: To easily peel garlic, place a clove on a cutting board. Cover the clove with the flat side of a chef's knife blade, then firmly press down on the blade with your fist. This loosens the skin so that it comes right off.

Mediterranean Vegetable Sandwich

Mediterranean Vegetable Sandwiches

1 small eggplant, peeled, halved, cut
    into ¼-inch-thick slices
    Salt
1 small zucchini, halved, cut lengthwise
    into ¼-inch-thick slices
1 green or red bell pepper, sliced
3 tablespoons balsamic vinegar
½ teaspoon salt
½ teaspoon garlic powder
2 French bread rolls, halved

1. Place eggplant in nonaluminum colander; sprinkle eggplant with salt. Let stand 30 minutes to drain. Rinse eggplant; pat dry with paper towels.

2. Preheat broiler. Spray rack of broiler pan with nonstick cooking spray. Place vegetables on rack. Broil 4 inches from heat, 8 to 10 minutes or until vegetables are browned, turning once.

3. Combine vinegar, ½ teaspoon salt and garlic powder in medium bowl until well blended. Add vegetables; toss to coat. Spoon vegetable mixture evenly into rolls. Garnish with apple slices, if desired. Serve immediately. *Makes 2 servings*

Dietary Exchanges per Serving:
1½ Starch/Bread, 3 Vegetable

NUTRIENTS PER SERVING:

Calories	178
% calories from fat	10
Total Fat	2 g
Saturated Fat	<1 g
Cholesterol	0 mg
Sodium	775 mg
Carbohydrate	36 g
Dietary Fiber	1 g
Protein	5 g
Calcium	58 mg
Iron	3 mg
Vitamin A	52 RE
Vitamin C	44 mg

New York-Style Spinach Pizza

1 package (10 ounces) refrigerated
   pizza crust
1 tablespoon cornmeal
3 teaspoons vegetable oil, divided
4 cloves garlic, finely chopped
1 package (10 ounces) frozen chopped
   spinach, thawed, drained
2 tomatoes, thinly sliced
1 cup sliced mushrooms
1 cup (4 ounces) shredded part-skim
   mozzarella cheese
¼ cup chopped fresh basil *or*
   1 tablespoon dried basil leaves

1. Preheat oven to 450°F. Prepare pizza crust according to package directions. Sprinkle cornmeal over large pizza pan or large baking sheet. Place pizza crust on pan.

2. Heat 1 teaspoon oil in large nonstick skillet over medium heat until hot. Add garlic. Cook and stir 5 minutes or until garlic is tender. Add spinach. Cook and stir 1 minute or until spinach is wilted.

3. Brush pizza crust with remaining 2 teaspoons oil. Spoon spinach mixture evenly over crust. Layer tomatoes, mushrooms, cheese and basil over spinach mixture.

4. Bake 20 minutes or until crust is golden brown and cheese melts.

Makes 8 servings

Dietary Exchanges per Serving:
1 Starch/Bread, ½ Lean Meat, 1 Vegetable, ½ Fat

NUTRIENTS PER SERVING:

Calories	162
% calories from fat	29
Total Fat	5 g
Saturated Fat	2 g
Cholesterol	8 mg
Sodium	260 mg
Carbohydrate	21 g
Dietary Fiber	1 g
Protein	8 g
Calcium	133 mg
Iron	2 mg
Vitamin A	229 RE
Vitamin C	10 mg

Trail Mix Truffles

⅓ cup dried apples
¼ cup dried apricots
¼ cup apple butter
2 tablespoons golden raisins
1 tablespoon reduced fat peanut butter
½ cup low fat granola
¼ cup graham cracker crumbs, divided
¼ cup mini semisweet chocolate chips

1. In food processor or blender combine apples, apricots, apple butter, raisins and peanut butter; process until smooth. Stir in granola, 1 tablespoon graham cracker crumbs, mini chips and 1 tablespoon water until soft dough forms.

2. Place remaining graham cracker crumbs in small bowl. Shape 1 tablespoon fruit mixture into ball; roll in crumbs to coat. Repeat. Cover; refrigerate until ready to serve.

Makes about 16 truffles

Dietary Exchanges per Serving:
1 Starch/Bread, ½ Fruit, ½ Fat

NUTRIENTS PER SERVING:
2 truffles

Calories	121
% calories from fat	30
Total Fat	4 g
Saturated Fat	1 g
Cholesterol	0 mg
Sodium	14 mg
Carbohydrate	20 g
Dietary Fiber	2 g
Protein	3 g
Calcium	49 mg
Iron	1 mg
Vitamin A	30 RE
Vitamin C	1 mg

Miniature Fruit Muffins

1 cup whole wheat flour
¾ cup all-purpose flour
½ cup packed dark brown sugar
2 teaspoons baking powder
½ teaspoon baking soda
¼ teaspoon salt
1 cup buttermilk, divided
¾ cup frozen blueberries
1 small ripe banana, mashed
¼ teaspoon vanilla
⅓ cup unsweetened applesauce
2 tablespoons raisins
½ teaspoon ground cinnamon

1. Preheat oven to 400°F. Spray 36 miniature muffin cups with nonstick cooking spray; set aside.

2. Combine flours, sugar, baking powder, baking soda and salt in medium bowl. Add ⅓ cup dry ingredients to each of 2 small bowls.

3. To one portion flour mixture, add ⅓ cup buttermilk and blueberries. Stir just until blended; spoon into 12 prepared muffin cups. To second portion, add ⅓ cup buttermilk, banana and vanilla. Stir just until blended; spoon into 12 muffin cups. To final portion, add remaining ⅓ cup buttermilk, applesauce, raisins and cinnamon. Stir just until blended; spoon into 12 muffin cups.

4. Bake 18 minutes or until lightly browned and wooden pick inserted into centers comes out clean. Remove from pan. Cool 10 minutes on wire racks. Serve warm or cool completely.   *Makes 12 servings*

Dietary Exchanges per Serving:
1 Starch/Bread, 1 Fruit

NUTRIENTS PER SERVING:
3 miniature muffins

Calories	130
% calories from fat	4
Total Fat	1 g
Saturated Fat	<1 g
Cholesterol	1 mg
Sodium	178 mg
Carbohydrate	29 g
Dietary Fiber	2 g
Protein	3 g
Calcium	49 mg
Iron	1 mg
Vitamin A	4 RE
Vitamin C	2 mg

English Muffin Turkey Sandwiches

2 raisin English muffins, halved
4 teaspoons Dijon mustard
4 tomato slices
4 red onion slices
4 ounces thinly sliced turkey breast
1 cup (4 ounces) shredded part-skim
    mozzarella cheese
1 cup alfalfa sprouts

1. Preheat oven to 400°F. Place English muffin halves on baking sheet. Spread mustard evenly over halves. Layer tomato, onion, turkey and cheese evenly over halves.

2. Bake English muffin halves 4 minutes or until cheese melts. Top each serving evenly with alfalfa sprouts before serving.
Makes 4 servings

Dietary Exchanges per Serving:
1 Starch/Bread, 2 Lean Meat

NUTRIENTS PER SERVING:

Calories	183
% calories from fat	29
Total Fat	6 g
Saturated Fat	3 g
Cholesterol	31 mg
Sodium	586 mg
Carbohydrate	17 g
Dietary Fiber	1 g
Protein	15 g
Calcium	233 mg
Iron	1 mg
Vitamin A	71 RE
Vitamin C	4 mg

Bruschetta

Nonstick cooking spray
1 cup thinly sliced onion
½ cup chopped seeded tomato
2 tablespoons capers, rinsed and drained
¼ teaspoon ground black pepper
3 cloves garlic, finely chopped
1 teaspoon olive oil
4 slices (about 1 inch thick) Italian or French bread
½ cup (2 ounces) shredded reduced fat Monterey Jack cheese

1. Spray large nonstick skillet with cooking spray. Heat over medium heat until hot. Add onion. Cook and stir 5 minutes or until onion is tender. Stir in tomato, capers and pepper. Cook 3 minutes or until heated through, stirring occasionally.

2. Preheat broiler. Combine garlic and oil in small bowl. Brush oil mixture over bread slices. Spoon onion mixture evenly over slices; sprinkle evenly with cheese. Place slices on baking sheet. Broil 3 minutes or until cheese melts. Garnish as desired. Serve immediately. *Makes 4 servings*

Dietary Exchanges per Serving:
1 Starch/Bread

NUTRIENTS PER SERVING:
1 tablespoon topping, 1 slice bread

Calories	90
% calories from fat	20
Total Fat	2 g
Saturated Fat	<1 g
Cholesterol	0 mg
Sodium	194 mg
Carbohydrate	17 g
Dietary Fiber	<1 g
Protein	3 g
Calcium	25 mg
Iron	7 mg
Vitamin A	6 RE
Vitamin C	3 mg

Pepper-Cheese Polenta

¾ teaspoon sugar
¼ teaspoon salt
⅓ cup yellow or white cornmeal
¼ cup chopped red or green bell pepper
½ cup (2 ounces) shredded reduced fat Monterey Jack cheese

1. Spray 8½ × 4½-inch loaf pan with nonstick cooking spray; set aside.

2. Combine 1 cup water, sugar and salt in small saucepan. Bring to a boil over high heat. Stir in cornmeal with wire whisk. Reduce heat to medium. Cook 10 minutes or until mixture thickens and pulls away from side of pan, stirring constantly.

3. Spoon polenta into prepared pan; cover. Refrigerate 1 hour or until firm.

4. Preheat broiler. Cut polenta into 4 slices. Sprinkle pepper and cheese evenly over slices. Place slices on baking sheet. Broil 3 to 5 minutes or until cheese melts. Serve immediately. *Makes 4 servings*

Dietary Exchanges per Serving:
½ Starch/Bread, ½ Lean Meat, ½ Fat

NUTRIENTS PER SERVING:

Calories	84
% calories from fat	30
Total Fat	3 g
Saturated Fat	2 g
Cholesterol	10 mg
Sodium	249 mg
Carbohydrate	10 g
Dietary Fiber	2 g
Protein	6 g
Calcium	129 mg
Iron	<1 mg
Vitamin A	44 RE
Vitamin C	13 mg

Bruschetta

South-of-the-Border Nachos

4 ounces low fat tortilla chips
  Nonstick cooking spray
¾ cup chopped onion
2 jalapeño peppers, seeded, chopped*
3 cloves garlic, finely chopped
2 teaspoons chili powder
½ teaspoon ground cumin
1 boneless skinless chicken breast
  (about 6 ounces), cooked, chopped
1 can (14½ ounces) Mexican-style diced
  tomatoes, drained
1 cup (4 ounces) shredded reduced fat
  Monterey Jack cheese
2 tablespoons black olives, chopped

*Jalapeño peppers can sting and irritate the skin. Wear rubber gloves when handling peppers and do not touch eyes.

1. Preheat oven to 350°F. Place chips on 13 × 9-inch baking pan.

2. Spray large nonstick skillet with cooking spray. Heat over medium heat until hot. Add onion, peppers, garlic, chili powder and cumin. Cook and stir 5 minutes or until vegetables are tender. Stir in chicken and tomatoes.

3. Spoon tomato mixture, cheese and olives over chips. Bake 5 minutes or until cheese melts. *Makes 4 servings*

Dietary Exchanges per Serving:
1 Starch/Bread, 2 Lean Meat, 1 Vegetable, ½ Fat

NUTRIENTS PER SERVING:

Calories	226
% calories from fat	26
Total Fat	7 g
Saturated Fat	2 g
Cholesterol	34 mg
Sodium	273 mg
Carbohydrate	21 g
Dietary Fiber	2 g
Protein	22 g
Calcium	377 mg
Iron	2 mg
Vitamin A	137 RE
Vitamin C	44 mg

Italian Stuffed Mushrooms

8 large mushrooms
  Nonstick cooking spray
2 ounces lean ground pork
½ cup whole wheat bread crumbs
1 egg white
2 green onions, finely chopped
1 teaspoon dried oregano leaves
¼ teaspoon ground black pepper
½ cup (2 ounces) shredded nonfat
  mozzarella cheese

1. Preheat oven to 350°F.

2. Remove stems from mushrooms; set caps aside. Finely chop stems.

3. Spray small nonstick skillet with cooking spray. Heat over medium heat until hot. Add chopped stems and pork. Cook and stir 5 minutes or until pork is no longer pink.

4. Combine pork mixture, bread crumbs, egg white, onions, oregano and pepper in medium bowl until well blended. Spoon pork mixture evenly into mushroom caps, mounding slightly in center. Place caps on baking sheet. Sprinkle cheese evenly over tops of mushrooms.

5. Bake 15 minutes or until mushrooms are tender. Serve immediately.
Makes 4 servings

Dietary Exchanges per Serving:
1 Lean Meat, 1 Vegetable

NUTRIENTS PER SERVING:

Calories	69
% calories from fat	16
Total Fat	1 g
Saturated Fat	<1 g
Cholesterol	11 mg
Sodium	153 mg
Carbohydrate	5 g
Dietary Fiber	1 g
Protein	10 g
Calcium	146 mg
Iron	1 mg
Vitamin A	46 RE
Vitamin C	2 mg

Roasted Eggplant Spread

Roasted Eggplant Spread

  1 **large eggplant**
  1 **can (14½ ounces) diced tomatoes,**
    drained
  ½ **cup finely chopped green onions**
  ½ **cup chopped fresh parsley**
  2 **tablespoons red wine vinegar**
  1 **tablespoon olive oil**
  3 **cloves garlic, finely chopped**
  ½ **teaspoon salt**
  ½ **teaspoon dried oregano leaves**
  2 **pita breads**

1. Preheat oven to 375°F.

2. Place eggplant on baking sheet. Bake
1 hour or until tender, turning occasionally.
Remove eggplant from oven. Let stand
10 minutes or until cool enough to handle.

3. Cut eggplant lengthwise in half; remove
pulp. Place pulp in medium bowl; mash with
fork until smooth. Add tomatoes, onions,
parsley, vinegar, oil, garlic, salt and oregano;
blend well. Cover eggplant mixture;
refrigerate 2 hours.

4. Preheat broiler. Split pita breads
horizontally in half to form 4 rounds. Stack
rounds; cut into sixths to form 24 wedges.

Place wedges on baking sheet. Broil 3
minutes or until crisp.

5. Serve eggplant mixture with warm pita
bread wedges. Garnish with lemon and lime
slices, if desired. *Makes 4 servings*

Dietary Exchanges per Serving:
1 Starch/Bread, 1 Vegetable, ½ Fat

NUTRIENTS PER SERVING:
6 pita bread wedges; ½ cup eggplant spread

Calories	134
% calories from fat	20
Total Fat	3 g
Saturated Fat	<1 g
Cholesterol	0 mg
Sodium	347 mg
Carbohydrate	23 g
Dietary Fiber	3 g
Protein	4 g
Calcium	49 mg
Iron	2 mg
Vitamin A	87 RE
Vitamin C	18 mg

Egg Rolls

Sweet and Sour Sauce (recipe follows)
Nonstick cooking spray
3 green onions, finely chopped
3 cloves garlic, finely chopped
½ teaspoon ground ginger
½ pound boneless skinless chicken breasts, cooked, finely chopped
2 cups bean sprouts, rinsed, drained
½ cup shredded carrot
2 tablespoons reduced sodium soy sauce
¼ teaspoon ground black pepper
8 egg roll wrappers
2 teaspoons vegetable oil

1. Prepare Sweet and Sour Sauce.

2. Spray large nonstick skillet with cooking spray. Heat over medium-high heat until hot. Add onions, garlic and ginger. Cook and stir 1 minute. Add chicken, bean sprouts and carrot. Cook and stir 2 minutes. Stir in soy sauce and pepper. Cook and stir 1 minute. Remove skillet from heat. Let mixture stand 10 minutes or until cool enough to handle.

3. Brush edges of egg roll wrappers with water. Spoon filling evenly down centers of wrappers. Fold ends over filling; roll up jelly-roll fashion.

4. Heat oil in another large nonstick skillet over medium heat until hot. Add egg rolls. Cook 3 to 5 minutes or until golden brown, turning occasionally. Serve hot with Sweet and Sour Sauce.   *Makes 8 Egg Rolls*

Sweet and Sour Sauce

4 teaspoons cornstarch
1 cup water
½ cup sugar
½ cup white vinegar
¼ cup tomato paste

Combine all ingredients in small saucepan. Bring to a boil over high heat, stirring constantly. Boil 1 minute, stirring constantly. Cool.   *Makes about 1½ cups (4 servings)*

Dietary Exchanges per Serving:
1 Starch/Bread, 2 Lean Meat, 2 Vegetable

NUTRIENTS PER SERVING:
2 Egg Rolls

Calories	335
% calories from fat	13
Total Fat	5 g
Saturated Fat	<1 g
Cholesterol	48 mg
Sodium	465 mg
Carbohydrate	62 g
Dietary Fiber	5 g
Protein	25 g
Calcium	38 mg
Iron	3 mg
Vitamin A	455 RE
Vitamin C	17 mg

Health Note: Canola oil has the lowest percentage of saturated fat of any vegetable oil. Saturated fat interferes with the removal of excess fat and cholesterol from the body and should comprise only 10 percent of total calories (approximately 20 g for a 2,000 calorie diet).

Bean & Cheese Quesadillas

Spicy Salsa (recipe follows)
½ cup nonfat ricotta cheese
4 (6-inch) flour tortillas
½ cup rinsed, drained pinto beans, cooked, mashed
½ cup (2 ounces) shredded reduced fat Monterey Jack cheese
Nonstick cooking spray

1. Prepare Spicy Salsa.

2. Spread ricotta cheese evenly over half of each tortilla. Layer beans, Monterey Jack cheese, and ½ cup salsa evenly over ricotta cheese. Fold in half.

3. Spray small nonstick skillet with cooking spray. Heat over medium-high heat until hot. Place tortillas in skillet, one at a time. Cook 4 minutes or until golden brown and cheese melts, turning once. Cut tortillas in half. Serve with remaining 1½ cups Spicy Salsa
Makes 4 servings

Spicy Salsa

1 cup chopped seeded tomato
¼ cup finely chopped green onions
¼ cup finely chopped fresh cilantro
2 tablespoons lime juice
1 jalapeño pepper, seeded, finely chopped*
2 cloves garlic, finely chopped

*Jalapeño peppers can sting and irritate the skin. Wear rubber gloves when handling peppers and do not touch eyes.

Combine all ingredients in small bowl until well blended. Let stand 1 hour.
Makes about 2 cups

Dietary Exchanges per Serving:
2½ Starch/Bread, 1 Fat

NUTRIENTS PER SERVING:

Calories	237
% calories from fat	26
Total Fat	7 g
Saturated Fat	3 g
Cholesterol	20 mg
Sodium	265 mg
Carbohydrate	31 g
Dietary Fiber	3 g
Protein	14 g
Calcium	235 mg
Iron	1 mg
Vitamin A	147 RE
Vitamin C	17 mg

Yogurt Spinach Dip

1 cup plain low fat yogurt
¼ cup cooked fresh or frozen chopped spinach, drained
½ teaspoon ground cumin

1. Combine yogurt, spinach and cumin in medium bowl until well blended.

2. Line sieve or strainer with cheesecloth or coffee filter; place sieve over large bowl. Spoon yogurt mixture into sieve; cover. Refrigerate 24 hours or until desired consistency is reached. Remove sieve from bowl; discard liquid. Invert sieve over serving plate. Serve dip with fresh vegetables, if desired. *Makes ¾ cup (4 servings)*

Dietary Exchanges per Serving:
½ Milk

NUTRIENTS PER SERVING:
3 tablespoons

Calories	40
% calories from fat	22
Total Fat	1 g
Saturated Fat	1 g
Cholesterol	4 mg
Sodium	48 mg
Carbohydrate	5 g
Dietary Fiber	<1 g
Protein	3 g
Calcium	122 mg
Iron	<1 g
Vitamin A	104 RE
Vitamin C	2 mg

Tuna Salad Pita Pockets

1 can (9 ounces) water-packed tuna,
    rinsed, drained, flaked
1 cup chopped peeled cucumber
¼ cup part-skim ricotta cheese
2 tablespoons reduced-fat mayonnaise
2 tablespoons red wine vinegar
2 green onions, chopped
1 tablespoon sweet pickle relish
2 cloves garlic, finely chopped
½ teaspoon salt
¼ teaspoon ground black pepper
1 cup alfalfa sprouts
2 whole wheat pita breads, cut
    crosswise in half

1. Combine tuna, cucumber, cheese, mayonnaise, vinegar, onions, relish, garlic, salt and pepper in medium bowl; blend well.

2. Divide alfalfa sprouts evenly among pita bread halves. Spoon tuna mixture evenly into halves. Garnish as desired.

Makes 4 servings

Dietary Exchanges per Serving:
1½ Starch/Bread, 2 Lean Meat

NUTRIENTS PER SERVING:

Calories	209
% calories from fat	18
Total Fat	4 g
Saturated Fat	1 g
Cholesterol	22 mg
Sodium	752 mg
Carbohydrate	22 g
Dietary Fiber	<1 g
Protein	22 g
Calcium	55 mg
Iron	1 mg
Vitamin A	44 RE
Vitamin C	4 mg

Cheesy Potato Skins

4 baking potatoes, scrubbed
2 tablespoons grated Parmesan cheese
3 cloves garlic, finely chopped
2 teaspoons dried rosemary
½ teaspoon salt
¼ teaspoon ground black pepper
2 egg whites, slightly beaten
½ cup (2 ounces) shredded part-skim
    mozzarella cheese
    Prepared salsa (optional)

1. Preheat oven to 425°F.

2. Prick potatoes with fork; place on baking sheet. Bake 45 minutes or until tender. Remove potatoes from oven. Let stand 10 minutes or until cool enough to handle. Meanwhile, combine Parmesan cheese, garlic, rosemary, salt and pepper in small bowl; set aside.

3. *Reduce oven temperature to 400°F.* Cut potatoes lengthwise in half. Remove potato pulp with spoon, leaving ¼-inch-thick shells. (Reserve potato pulp for another use, if desired.) Cut shells lengthwise into 2 halves.

4. Place halves on baking sheet. Brush insides with egg whites; sprinkle Parmesan cheese mixture evenly over halves.

5. Bake 20 minutes; sprinkle halves with mozzarella cheese. Bake 5 minutes or until cheese melts. Serve with salsa, if desired.

Makes 8 servings

Dietary Exchanges per Serving:
1 Starch/Bread, ½ Lean Meat

NUTRIENTS PER SERVING:

Calories	90
% calories from fat	17
Total Fat	2 g
Saturated Fat	1 g
Cholesterol	5 mg
Sodium	215 mg
Carbohydrate	14 g
Dietary Fiber	2 g
Protein	5 g
Calcium	85 mg
Iron	2 mg
Vitamin A	17 RE
Vitamin C	5 mg

Tuna Salad Pita Pocket

Super Soups & Salads

Crunch your way through crispy salads or spoon into splendid soups for a refreshing change of pace. Enjoy them on their own or as an appetizing prelude to a meal.

Apple Slaw with Poppy Seed Dressing

1 cup coarsely chopped unpeeled Jonathan apple
1 teaspoon lemon juice
2 tablespoons nonfat sour cream
4½ teaspoons skim milk
1 tablespoon frozen apple juice concentrate, thawed
1 teaspoon sugar
¾ teaspoon poppy seeds
½ cup sliced carrot
⅓ cup shredded green cabbage
⅓ cup shredded red cabbage
2 tablespoons finely chopped green bell pepper

1. Combine apple and lemon juice in resealable plastic food storage bag. Seal bag; toss to coat.

2. Combine sour cream, milk, apple juice concentrate, sugar and poppy seeds in small bowl until well blended. Add apple mixture, carrot, cabbages and pepper; toss to coat. Serve over cabbage leaves, if desired.

Makes 2 servings

Dietary Exchanges per Serving:
1 Fruit, 1 Vegetable

NUTRIENTS PER SERVING:

Calories	94
% calories from fat	7
Total Fat	1 g
Saturated Fat	<1 g
Cholesterol	<1 mg
Sodium	34 mg
Carbohydrate	21 g
Dietary Fiber	2 g
Protein	3 g
Calcium	92 mg
Iron	1 mg
Vitamin A	375 RE
Vitamin C	44 mg

Apple Slaw with Poppy Seed Dressing

Zesty Taco Salad

2 tablespoons vegetable oil
1 clove garlic, finely chopped
¾ pound ground turkey
1¾ teaspoons chili powder
¼ teaspoon ground cumin
3 cups washed, torn lettuce leaves
1 can (14½ ounces) Mexican-style diced
   tomatoes, drained
1 cup rinsed, drained canned garbanzo
   beans (chick-peas) or pinto beans
⅔ cup chopped peeled cucumber
⅓ cup frozen whole kernel corn, thawed
¼ cup chopped red onion
1 to 2 jalapeño peppers, seeded, finely
   chopped* (optional)
1 tablespoon red wine vinegar
12 nonfat tortilla chips

*Jalapeño peppers can sting and irritate the skin. Wear rubber gloves when handling peppers and do not touch eyes.

1. Combine oil and garlic in small bowl; let stand 1 hour at room temperature.

2. Combine turkey, chili powder and cumin in large nonstick skillet. Cook over medium heat 5 minutes or until turkey is no longer pink, stirring to crumble.

3. Combine turkey, lettuce, tomatoes, beans, cucumber, corn, onion and jalapeño in large bowl. Remove garlic from oil; discard garlic. Combine oil and vinegar in small bowl. Drizzle over salad; toss to coat. Serve over tortilla chips. Serve with additional tortilla chips, if desired. *Makes 4 servings*

Dietary Exchanges per Serving:
1½ Starch/Bread, 2 Lean Meat, 1 Vegetable, 1 Fat

NUTRIENTS PER SERVING:

Calories	285
% calories from fat	33
Total Fat	11 g
Saturated Fat	1 g
Cholesterol	33 mg
Sodium	484 mg
Carbohydrate	28 g
Dietary Fiber	5 g
Protein	21 g
Calcium	77 mg
Iron	3 mg
Vitamin A	123 RE
Vitamin C	23 mg

Salmon Pasta Salad

2 tablespoons fat free mayonnaise
3 teaspoons lemon juice
2 teaspoons capers, rinsed and drained
⅛ teaspoon paprika
1 cup cooked medium shell pasta
1 can (6 ounces) canned red salmon or
   tuna, rinsed, drained, flaked
½ cup finely chopped celery
2 tablespoons finely chopped red bell
   pepper
1 green onion, finely chopped
2 tablespoons chopped fresh parsley

Combine mayonnaise, lemon juice, capers and paprika in medium bowl. Add pasta, salmon, celery, pepper and onion; toss to coat. Cover; refrigerate 2 hours before serving. Top each serving evenly with parsley. *Makes 2 servings*

Dietary Exchanges per Serving:
1½ Starch/Bread, 2 Lean Meat, 1 Vegetable, ½ Fat

NUTRIENTS PER SERVING:

Calories	262
% calories from fat	32
Total Fat	9 g
Saturated Fat	2 g
Cholesterol	21 mg
Sodium	627 mg
Carbohydrate	26 g
Dietary Fiber	2 g
Protein	18 g
Calcium	216 mg
Iron	2 mg
Vitamin A	153 RE
Vitamin C	44 mg

Easy Fish Soup

1 cube low sodium vegetable bouillon
1 rib celery, cut into 2-inch slices
1 carrot, cut into 1-inch slices
½ cup bottled clam juice
½ teaspoon lemon juice
¼ cup chopped onion
2 sprigs fresh parsley
½ bay leaf
¼ teaspoon dried thyme leaves
⅛ teaspoon dried oregano leaves
2 teaspoons reduced calorie margarine
½ teaspoon finely chopped garlic
1 medium tomato, peeled, seeded,
    coarsely chopped
½ cup cubed peeled potato
¼ cup chopped red onion
2 tablespoons finely chopped carrot
1 lean whitefish fillet (about 6 ounces),
    cut into 1-inch pieces
2 teaspoons finely chopped fresh
    parsley
½ teaspoon grated lemon peel

1. Combine 1 cup water and bouillon in medium saucepan. Bring to a boil over high heat. Add celery, carrot slices, clam juice, lemon juice, onion, parsley sprigs, bay leaf, thyme and oregano. Bring to a boil over high heat, stirring occasionally. Reduce heat to medium-low. Simmer 20 minutes, stirring occasionally.

2. Meanwhile, melt margarine in large nonstick saucepan over medium-high heat. Add garlic. Cook and stir 2 minutes. Add tomato, potato, red onion and finely chopped carrot. Cook and stir 3 minutes.

3. Strain bouillon mixture; discard solids. Add bouillon mixture and fish to saucepan. Cook over medium heat 8 minutes or until potato is tender and fish is opaque, stirring occasionally.

4. Top each serving evenly with finely chopped parsley and lemon peel.

Makes 2 servings

Dietary Exchanges per Serving:
½ Starch/Bread, 2 Lean Meat, 2 Vegetable

NUTRIENTS PER SERVING:

Calories	185
% calories from fat	15
Total Fat	3 g
Saturated Fat	1 g
Cholesterol	30 mg
Sodium	480 mg
Carbohydrate	25 g
Dietary Fiber	4 g
Protein	16 g
Calcium	60 mg
Iron	2 mg
Vitamin A	1,326 RE
Vitamin C	33 mg

Cook's Tip: Lean fish, classified as those that have a fat content of less than 3 percent of total calories, include sea bass, cod, haddock, pollock and perch. When buying fresh fish, purchase fillets that have a firm texture, a moist appearance and a fresh odor; immediately refrigerate fillets and use within 2 days.

Roasted Winter Vegetable Soup

1 small or ½ medium acorn squash, halved
2 medium tomatoes
1 medium onion, unpeeled
1 green bell pepper, halved
1 red bell pepper, halved
2 small red potatoes
3 cloves garlic, unpeeled
1½ cups tomato juice
4 teaspoons vegetable oil
1 tablespoon red wine vinegar
¼ teaspoon ground black pepper
¾ cup chopped fresh cilantro, divided
4 tablespoons nonfat sour cream

1. Preheat oven to 400°F. Spray baking sheet with nonstick cooking spray.

2. Place acorn squash, tomatoes, onion, bell peppers, potatoes and garlic on prepared baking sheet. Bake 40 minutes, removing garlic and tomatoes after 10 minutes. Remove remaining vegetables from oven. Let stand 15 minutes or until cool enough to handle.

3. Peel vegetables; discard skins. Coarsely chop vegetables. In food processor or blender combine ½ of chopped vegetables, tomato juice, ½ cup water, oil and vinegar; process until smooth.

4. Combine vegetable mixture, remaining chopped vegetables and black pepper in large saucepan. Bring to a simmer over medium-high heat. Simmer 5 minutes or until heated through, stirring constantly.

5. Top each serving evenly with cilantro and sour cream. *Makes 4 servings*

Dietary Exchanges per Serving:
1½ Starch/Bread, 2 Vegetable, 1 Fat

NUTRIENTS PER SERVING:

Calories	193
% calories from fat	22
Total Fat	5 g
Saturated Fat	<1 g
Cholesterol	0 mg
Sodium	345 mg
Carbohydrate	36 g
Dietary Fiber	5 g
Protein	5 g
Calcium	84 mg
Iron	2 mg
Vitamin A	330 RE
Vitamin C	92 mg

Pasta & Cabbage Salad

1½ teaspoons cider vinegar
1 teaspoon sugar
⅛ teaspoon salt
⅛ teaspoon ground black pepper
⅛ teaspoon prepared yellow mustard
1 tablespoon nonfat sour cream
2¼ teaspoons evaporated skim milk
1 cup cooked bow tie pasta
⅔ cup shredded green cabbage
⅓ cup halved sliced zucchini
4 cherry tomatoes, halved
1 green onion, finely chopped

Combine vinegar, sugar, salt, pepper and mustard in small bowl. Stir in sour cream and milk until well blended. Add pasta, cabbage, zucchini, tomatoes and onion; toss to coat. Cover; refrigerate 2 hours before serving. *Makes 2 servings*

Dietary Exchanges per Serving:
1 Starch/Bread, 1 Vegetable

NUTRIENTS PER SERVING:

Calories	102
% calories from fat	5
Total Fat	1 g
Saturated Fat	<1 g
Cholesterol	<1 mg
Sodium	161 mg
Carbohydrate	21 g
Dietary Fiber	2 g
Protein	4 g
Calcium	50 mg
Iron	1 mg
Vitamin A	97 RE
Vitamin C	29 mg

Vegetarian Chili

1 tablespoon vegetable oil
2 cloves garlic, finely chopped
1½ cups thinly sliced mushrooms
⅔ cup chopped red onion
⅔ cup chopped red bell pepper
2 teaspoons chili powder
¼ teaspoon ground cumin
⅛ teaspoon ground red pepper
⅛ teaspoon dried oregano leaves
1 can (28 ounces) peeled whole
   tomatoes, undrained
⅔ cup frozen baby lima beans
½ cup rinsed, drained canned Great
   Northern beans
3 tablespoons nonfat sour cream
3 tablespoons shredded reduced fat
   Cheddar cheese

1. Heat oil in large nonstick saucepan over medium-high heat until hot. Add garlic. Cook and stir 3 minutes. Add mushrooms, onion and bell pepper. Cook and stir 5 minutes. Add chili powder, cumin, red pepper and oregano. Cook and stir 1 minute. Add

tomatoes with liquid and beans. Reduce heat to medium-low. Simmer 15 minutes, stirring occasionally.

2. Top each serving evenly with sour cream and cheese. *Makes 4 servings*

Dietary Exchanges per Serving:
1 Starch/Bread, 3 Vegetable, 1 Fat

NUTRIENTS PER SERVING:

Calories	189
% calories from fat	24
Total Fat	5 g
Saturated Fat	1 g
Cholesterol	3 mg
Sodium	428 mg
Carbohydrate	29 g
Dietary Fiber	7 g
Protein	10 g
Calcium	154 mg
Iron	4 mg
Vitamin A	467 RE
Vitamin C	121 mg

Three Bean Salad

2 tablespoons reduced calorie
   mayonnaise
2 tablespoons nonfat sour cream
4 teaspoons cider vinegar
1 teaspoon sugar
¼ teaspoon ground black pepper
1 cup chopped celery
⅔ cup rinsed, drained canned garbanzo
   beans (chick-peas)
⅔ cup rinsed, drained canned pinto
   beans
⅔ cup rinsed, drained canned Italian
   broad beans
½ cup chopped green bell pepper
1 green onion, finely chopped
2 tablespoons chopped fresh parsley

1. Combine mayonnaise, sour cream, vinegar, sugar and black pepper in medium bowl until well blended. Add celery, beans, bell pepper and onion; toss to coat. Cover; refrigerate 2 hours before serving.

2. Top each serving evenly with parsley.
Makes 4 servings

Dietary Exchanges per Serving:
1½ Starch/Bread, 1 Vegetable, ½ Fat

NUTRIENTS PER SERVING:

Calories	158
% calories from fat	17
Total Fat	3 g
Saturated Fat	1 g
Cholesterol	0 mg
Sodium	632 mg
Carbohydrate	26 g
Dietary Fiber	5 g
Protein	8 g
Calcium	72 mg
Iron	3 mg
Vitamin A	228 RE
Vitamin C	72 mg

Vegetarian Chili

Sunburst Chicken Salad

1 tablespoon fat free mayonnaise
1 tablespoon nonfat sour cream
2 teaspoons frozen orange juice
   concentrate, thawed
¼ teaspoon grated orange peel
1 boneless skinless chicken breast
   (about 6 ounces), cooked, coarsely
   chopped
1 large kiwi, peeled, thinly sliced
⅓ cup tangerine or mandarin orange
   sections, halved
¼ cup finely chopped celery
4 lettuce leaves, washed
2 tablespoons coarsely chopped
   cashews

1. Combine mayonnaise, sour cream, orange juice concentrate and orange peel in small bowl until well blended. Add chicken, kiwi, tangerine and celery; toss to coat. Cover; refrigerate 2 hours before serving.

2. Serve chicken mixture over lettuce leaves. Top each serving evenly with cashews. Garnish as desired. Serve immediately.
Makes 2 servings

Dietary Exchanges per Serving:
2 Lean Meat, 1 Fruit, ½ Fat

NUTRIENTS PER SERVING:

Calories	195
% calories from fat	29
Total Fat	6 g
Saturated Fat	1 g
Cholesterol	39 mg
Sodium	431 mg
Carbohydrate	18 g
Dietary Fiber	2 g
Protein	18 g
Calcium	55 mg
Iron	1 mg
Vitamin A	68 RE
Vitamin C	61 mg

Gazpacho

1 can (15 ounces) diced tomatoes,
   drained
1 cucumber, peeled, quartered
¼ green bell pepper, quartered
½ small onion, quartered
¼ cup reduced sodium vegetable juice
   cocktail
1 tablespoon red wine vinegar
1 clove garlic, finely chopped
   Pinch ground white pepper
2 ounces baked ham, cut into ¼-inch
   cubes
1 slice toasted whole wheat bread, cut
   into ½ × ½-inch cubes
¼ cup chopped unpeeled cucumber
2 tablespoons finely chopped fresh
   cilantro

1. In food processor or blender combine tomatoes, quartered cucumber, bell pepper, onion, vegetable juice, vinegar, garlic and white pepper; process until finely chopped. Cover; refrigerate 2 hours before serving.

2. Top each serving evenly with ham, bread cubes, chopped cucumber and cilantro.
Makes 2 servings

Dietary Exchanges per Serving:
½ Starch/Bread, 1 Lean Meat, 3 Vegetable

NUTRIENTS PER SERVING:

Calories	157
% calories from fat	15
Total Fat	3 g
Saturated Fat	1 g
Cholesterol	9 mg
Sodium	755 mg
Carbohydrate	25 g
Dietary Fiber	2 g
Protein	11 g
Calcium	107 mg
Iron	3 mg
Vitamin A	234 RE
Vitamin C	66 mg

Sunburst Chicken Salad

Mexicali Bean & Cheese Salad

1 teaspoon vegetable oil
1 clove garlic, finely chopped
¼ cup finely chopped red onion
1½ teaspoons chili powder
¼ teaspoon ground cumin
⅛ teaspoon crushed red pepper
1 cup frozen whole kernel corn, thawed
⅓ cup rinsed, drained canned pinto beans
⅓ cup rinsed, drained canned kidney beans
1 boneless skinless chicken breast (about 6 ounces), cooked, shredded
½ cup chopped seeded tomato
2 tablespoons drained canned diced mild green chilies
1 green onion, finely chopped
1 teaspoon lime juice
2 ounces reduced fat Monterey Jack cheese, cut into ⅓-inch cubes

1. Heat oil in medium nonstick skillet over medium heat until hot. Add garlic. Cook and stir 1 minute. Add red onion, chili powder, cumin and red pepper. Cook and stir 3 minutes. Add corn and beans. Cook and stir 2 minutes. Add chicken. Cook and stir 5 minutes or until heated through.

2. Spoon bean mixture into medium serving bowl. Add tomato, chilies, green onion and lime juice; toss to combine. Add cheese; toss to combine. Refrigerate 2 hours before serving.   *Makes 2 servings*

Dietary Exchanges per Serving:
2½ Starch/Bread, 3 Lean Meat, 1 Vegetable

NUTRIENTS PER SERVING:

Calories	336
% calories from fat	25
Total Fat	10 g
Saturated Fat	4 g
Cholesterol	72 mg
Sodium	606 mg
Carbohydrate	36 g
Dietary Fiber	6 g
Protein	36 g
Calcium	310 mg
Iron	3 mg
Vitamin A	189 RE
Vitamin C	41 mg

Thai Pasta Salad with Peanut Sauce

¼ cup evaporated skim milk
4½ teaspoons creamy peanut butter
4½ teaspoons finely chopped red onion
1 teaspoon lemon juice
¾ teaspoon brown sugar
½ teaspoon reduced sodium soy sauce
⅛ teaspoon crushed red pepper
½ teaspoon finely chopped fresh ginger
1 cup hot, cooked whole wheat spaghetti
2 teaspoons finely chopped green onion

1. Combine milk, peanut butter, red onion, lemon juice, sugar, soy sauce and red pepper in medium saucepan. Bring to a boil over high heat, stirring constantly. Boil 2 minutes, stirring constantly. Reduce heat to medium-low. Add ginger; blend well. Add spaghetti; toss to coat.

2. Top each serving evenly with green onion. Serve immediately.   *Makes 2 servings*

Dietary Exchanges per Serving:
1½ Starch/Bread, ½ Milk, 1 Fat

NUTRIENTS PER SERVING:

Calories	187
% calories from fat	26
Total Fat	6 g
Saturated Fat	1 g
Cholesterol	38 mg
Sodium	85 mg
Carbohydrate	27 g
Dietary Fiber	3 g
Protein	9 g
Calcium	111 mg
Iron	1 mg
Vitamin A	45 RE
Vitamin C	3 mg

Cream of Chicken Soup

1 cup uncooked white rice
3 cans (10¾ ounces each) ⅓-less salt chicken broth
1 skinless chicken breast (about 6 ounces)
1 rib celery, coarsely chopped
1 carrot, thinly sliced
¼ cup coarsely chopped onion
3 sprigs fresh parsley
1¼ cups evaporated skim milk
¼ teaspoon dried thyme leaves
⅛ teaspoon ground white pepper
⅛ teaspoon ground nutmeg
2 tablespoons finely chopped fresh parsley
1 green onion, finely chopped

1. Cook rice according to package directions; omitting salt.

2. Meanwhile, combine chicken broth and chicken in large saucepan. Bring to a boil over high heat. Reduce heat to medium-low. Simmer 10 minutes, skimming off any foam that rises to surface. Add celery, carrot, onion and parsley sprigs. Simmer 10 minutes or until chicken is no longer pink near bone and vegetables are tender, skimming off any foam that rises to surface.

3. Remove chicken breast from saucepan. Let stand 10 minutes or until cool enough to handle. Remove chicken from bone. Cut into 1-inch pieces.

4. Add rice, chicken pieces, milk, thyme, pepper and nutmeg to saucepan. Cook over medium-high heat 8 minutes or until soup thickens, stirring constantly.

5. Top each serving evenly with finely chopped parsley and green onion.

Makes 4 servings

Dietary Exchanges per Serving:
2½ Starch/Bread, 1½ Lean Meat, ½ Milk, 1 Vegetable

NUTRIENTS PER SERVING:

Calories	326
% calories from fat	11
Total Fat	4 g
Saturated Fat	1 g
Cholesterol	28 mg
Sodium	173 mg
Carbohydrate	50 g
Dietary Fiber	1 g
Protein	21 g
Calcium	277 mg
Iron	3 mg
Vitamin A	633 RE
Vitamin C	11 mg

Health Note: An estimated 50 percent of older adults rely on nonbulk forming laxatives for regularity. Frequent use of these laxatives lowers the level of the blood protein albumin. Research suggests that lower than normal albumin levels may increase your risk of heart disease and cancer. Instead, try a more natural approach to regularity—increase your intake of fluids and fiber-rich foods such as whole grains, fruits and vegetables, and increase your level of physical activity.

Clam Chowder

Clam Chowder

1 can (5 ounces) whole baby clams, undrained
1 potato, peeled, coarsely chopped
¼ cup finely chopped onion
⅔ cup evaporated skim milk
Pinch ground white pepper
Pinch dried thyme leaves
1 tablespoon reduced calorie margarine

1. Drain clams; reserve juice. Add enough water to reserved juice to measure ⅔ cup. Combine clam juice mixture, potato and onion in large saucepan. Bring to a boil over high heat. Reduce heat to medium-low. Simmer 8 minutes or until potato is tender.

2. Add milk, pepper and thyme to saucepan. Increase heat to medium-high. Cook and stir 2 minutes. Add margarine. Cook 5 minutes or until soup thickens, stirring occasionally. Stir in clams. Cook and stir 5 minutes or until clams are firm. Garnish as desired.

Makes 2 servings

Dietary Exchanges per Serving:
1 Starch/Bread, 1 Lean Meat, 1 Milk

NUTRIENTS PER SERVING:

Calories	204
% calories from fat	17
Total Fat	4 g
Saturated Fat	1 g
Cholesterol	47 mg
Sodium	205 mg
Carbohydrate	30 g
Dietary Fiber	1 g
Protein	14 g
Calcium	295 mg
Iron	3 mg
Vitamin A	164 RE
Vitamin C	9 mg

Waldorf Salad

1 unpeeled tart red apple, such as
  McIntosh, coarsely chopped
1 teaspoon fresh lemon juice
4 teaspoons frozen apple juice
  concentrate, thawed
1 tablespoon fat free mayonnaise
1 tablespoon nonfat sour cream
⅛ teaspoon paprika
½ cup finely chopped celery
6 large lettuce leaves, washed
5 teaspoons coarsely chopped walnuts

1. Combine apple and lemon juice in resealable plastic food storage bag. Seal bag; toss to coat.

2. Combine apple juice concentrate, mayonnaise, sour cream and paprika in medium bowl until well blended. Add apple mixture and celery; toss to coat. Cover; refrigerate 2 hours before serving.

3. Serve each salad over lettuce leaves. Top each serving evenly with walnuts.
Makes 2 servings

Dietary Exchanges per Serving:
1 Fruit, 1 Fat

NUTRIENTS PER SERVING:

Calories	115
% calories from fat	30
Total Fat	4 g
Saturated Fat	<1 g
Cholesterol	0 mg
Sodium	134 mg
Carbohydrate	19 g
Dietary Fiber	3 g
Protein	3 g
Calcium	43 mg
Iron	1 mg
Vitamin A	65 RE
Vitamin C	25 mg

Scandinavian Beef & Vegetable Soup

1 tablespoon reduced calorie margarine
¾ pound beef stew meat, cut into 1-inch
  pieces
4 cups ⅓-less-salt beef broth
⅔ cup coarsely chopped peeled potato
⅓ cup coarsely chopped peeled turnip
⅓ cup pearl onions
⅓ cup coarsely chopped carrot
1 bay leaf
½ teaspoon dried rosemary
¼ teaspoon ground allspice
⅛ teaspoon ground black pepper
4 teaspoons finely chopped fresh
  parsley

1. Melt margarine in large saucepan over medium heat. Add beef; cook and stir 5 minutes or until beef is browned. Add 8 cups water. Bring to a boil over high heat. Reduce heat to medium-low. Simmer 1 hour or until beef is tender, stirring occasionally and skimming off any foam and fat that rises to surface.

2. Add potato, turnip, onions, carrot, bay leaf, rosemary, allspice and pepper to saucepan. Bring to a boil over high heat, stirring occasionally. Reduce heat to medium-low. Simmer 15 minutes or until vegetables are tender, stirring occasionally and skimming off any foam that rises to surface. Remove and discard bay leaf.

3. Top each serving evenly with parsley before serving.
Makes 4 servings

Dietary Exchanges per Serving:
½ Starch/Bread, 2 Lean Meat, 1 Vegetable

NUTRIENTS PER SERVING:

Calories	186
% calories from fat	30
Total Fat	6 g
Saturated Fat	2 g
Cholesterol	50 mg
Sodium	141 mg
Carbohydrate	12 g
Dietary Fiber	1 g
Protein	20 g
Calcium	29 mg
Iron	2 mg
Vitamin A	298 RE
Vitamin C	8 mg

Delicious Dinners

Transform ho-hum meals into dynamite dinners with these mouthwatering entrées prepared with delicious Mexican, Oriental and Italian fixings.

Cashew Chicken

10 ounces boneless skinless chicken breasts, cut into 1 × ½-inch pieces
1 tablespoon cornstarch
1 tablespoon dry white wine
1 tablespoon reduced sodium soy sauce
½ teaspoon garlic powder
1 teaspoon vegetable oil
6 green onions, cut into 1-inch pieces
2 cups sliced mushrooms
1 red or green bell pepper, thinly sliced
1 can (6 ounces) sliced water chestnuts, rinsed and drained
2 tablespoons hoisin sauce (optional)
2 cups hot, cooked white rice
¼ cup roasted cashews

1. Place chicken in large resealable plastic food storage bag. Combine cornstarch, wine, soy sauce and garlic powder in small bowl; whisk until well blended. Pour over chicken pieces. Seal bag; toss to coat. Marinate in refrigerator 1 hour. Drain chicken; discard marinade.

2. Heat oil in wok or large nonstick skillet until hot. Add onions; stir-fry 1 minute. Add chicken; stir-fry 2 minutes or until browned. Add mushrooms, pepper and water chestnuts; stir-fry 3 minutes or until vegetables are crisp-tender and chicken is no longer pink in center. Stir in hoisin sauce; cook and stir 1 minute or until heated through.

3. Serve chicken and vegetables over rice. Top each serving evenly with cashews. Serve immediately.   *Makes 4 servings*

Dietary Exchanges per Serving:
1½ Starch/Bread, 2 Lean Meat, 1½ Vegetable, ½ Fat

NUTRIENTS PER SERVING:

Calories	274
% calories from fat	23
Total Fat	7 g
Saturated Fat	1 g
Cholesterol	36 mg
Sodium	83 mg
Carbohydrate	34 g
Dietary Fiber	3 g
Protein	18 g
Calcium	28 mg
Iron	3 mg
Vitamin A	52 RE
Vitamin C	22 mg

Cashew Chicken

Spinach-Stuffed Shells

Spinach-Stuffed Shells

 1 package (10 ounces) chopped frozen
   spinach, thawed and drained
1½ cups nonfat ricotta cheese
 ½ cup grated Parmesan cheese
 ½ cup cholesterol free egg substitute
 3 cloves garlic, finely chopped
 1 teaspoon dried oregano leaves
 ½ teaspoon salt
 ½ teaspoon dried basil leaves
 ½ teaspoon dried marjoram leaves
 ¼ teaspoon ground black pepper
24 cooked large shell pasta
 2 cans (14½ ounces each) crushed
   tomatoes, undrained
 1 cup (4 ounces) shredded reduced fat
   mozzarella cheese

1. Preheat oven to 350°F. Spray 13 × 9-inch baking pan with nonstick cooking spray.

2. Combine spinach, ricotta and Parmesan cheeses, egg substitute and seasonings in large bowl. Spoon into shells. Place shells in prepared pan. Top with tomatoes with liquid and mozzarella cheese. Bake 20 minutes or until cheese melts. *Makes 4 servings*

Dietary Exchanges per Serving:
3 Starch/Bread, 3 Lean Meat, 2 Vegetable

NUTRIENTS PER SERVING:

Calories	456
% calories from fat	20
Total Fat	11 g
Saturated Fat	6 g
Cholesterol	35 mg
Sodium	803 mg
Carbohydrate	57 g
Dietary Fiber	6 g
Protein	38 g
Calcium	684 mg
Iron	5 mg
Vitamin A	1,081 RE
Vitamin C	41 mg

Grilled Tuna Niçoise with Citrus Marinade

Citrus Marinade (recipe follows)
1 **tuna steak (about 1 pound)***
2 **cups green beans, trimmed, halved**
4 **cups romaine lettuce leaves, washed,**
   torn into small pieces
8 **small cooked red potatoes, quartered**
1 **cup chopped seeded tomato**
4 **cooked egg whites, chopped**
¼ **cup sliced red onion, halved**
2 **teaspoons chopped black olives**

*Marinate in refrigerator 1 hour for each inch of thickness.

1. Prepare Citrus Marinade; combine with tuna in large resealable plastic food storage bag. Seal bag; toss to coat. Marinate in refrigerator 1 hour, turning occasionally. Drain tuna; discard marinade.

2. To prevent sticking, spray grill with nonstick cooking spray. Prepare coals for grilling.

3. Place tuna on grill, 4 inches from hot coals. Grill 8 to 10 minutes or until tuna flakes easily when tested with fork, turning once. Or, place tuna on rack of broiler pan coated with nonstick cooking spray. Broil 4 inches from heat, 8 to 10 minutes or until tuna flakes easily when tested with fork. Slice tuna into ¼-inch-thick slices; set aside.

4. Place 2 cups water in large saucepan; bring to a boil over high heat. Add beans; cook 2 minutes. Drain; rinse with cold water and drain again.

5. Place lettuce on large serving platter. Arrange tuna, beans, potatoes, tomato, egg whites and onion over lettuce. Sprinkle olives evenly over each serving. Serve with low calorie salad dressing, if desired.

Makes 4 servings

Citrus Marinade

½ **cup fresh lime juice**
¼ **cup vegetable oil**
2 **green onions, chopped**
1 **teaspoon dried tarragon leaves**
¼ **teaspoon garlic powder**
¼ **teaspoon ground black pepper**

Combine all ingredients in small bowl until well blended.

Dietary Exchanges per Serving:
2 Starch/Bread, 3 Lean Meat, 2½ Vegetable

NUTRIENTS PER SERVING:

Calories	373
% calories from fat	16
Total Fat	7 g
Saturated Fat	1 g
Cholesterol	48 mg
Sodium	160 mg
Carbohydrate	45 g
Dietary Fiber	6 g
Protein	35 g
Calcium	92 mg
Iron	4 mg
Vitamin A	246 RE
Vitamin C	55 mg

Cook's Tip: Marinate tuna 1 hour and cook it 8 to 10 minutes for every inch of thickness. Begin checking for doneness after 8 minutes of cooking by inserting a fork into the thickest part of the fish. When the tuna is opaque and flakes easily, and the juices are milky white, it is finished cooking.

Arroz con Pollo

1 boneless skinless chicken breast
1 teaspoon vegetable oil
1 cup halved sliced onion
1 red bell pepper, thinly sliced
½ cup uncooked white rice
2 cloves garlic, finely chopped
1 cup chopped seeded tomato
¾ cup ⅓-less-salt chicken broth
¼ teaspoon ground turmeric
1 package (10 ounces) frozen green peas
¼ teaspoon dried oregano leaves
¼ teaspoon ground black pepper

1. Spray large nonstick skillet with nonstick cooking spray. Add chicken. Cook 10 minutes or until chicken is no longer pink in center, turning once. Remove chicken from skillet. Let stand 10 minutes or until cool enough to handle; chop.

2. Heat oil in same skillet over medium heat until hot. Add onion, bell pepper, rice and garlic. Cook 5 minutes or until rice is browned, stirring occasionally. Add chicken and tomato.

3. Combine chicken broth and turmeric in small bowl until well blended. Add to skillet. Bring to a boil over high heat; cover. Reduce heat to medium-low. Simmer 10 minutes. Stir in peas; cover. Simmer 10 minutes or until rice is tender. Stir in oregano and black pepper. Serve immediately.

Makes 4 servings

Dietary Exchanges per Serving:
2 Starch/Bread, 1 Lean Meat, 2 Vegetable

NUTRIENTS PER SERVING:

Calories	231
% calories from fat	11
Total Fat	3 g
Saturated Fat	<1 g
Cholesterol	22 mg
Sodium	94 mg
Carbohydrate	37 g
Dietary Fiber	5 g
Protein	15 g
Calcium	46 mg
Iron	3 mg
Vitamin A	202 RE
Vitamin C	63 mg

Beef Burritos

Nonstick cooking spray
10 ounces lean ground beef
½ cup chopped onion
3 cloves garlic, finely chopped
1 can (14½ ounces) Mexican-style diced tomatoes, drained
1 package (10 ounces) frozen whole kernel corn
¼ cup drained canned diced mild green chilies
1 tablespoon chili powder
1 teaspoon ground cumin
4 (6-inch) flour tortillas

1. Spray large nonstick skillet with cooking spray. Heat over medium-high heat until hot. Add beef, onion and garlic. Cook and stir 5 minutes or until beef is no longer pink. Add tomatoes, corn, chilies, chili powder and cumin. Cook 5 minutes or until heated through, stirring occasionally.

2. Spoon beef mixture evenly down center of each tortilla. Fold bottom of tortillas over filling. Roll up burritos. Serve immediately.

Makes 4 servings

Dietary Exchanges per Serving:
2 Starch/Bread, 2 Lean Meat, 2½ Vegetable, ½ Fat

NUTRIENTS PER SERVING:

Calories	338
% calories from fat	28
Total Fat	11 g
Saturated Fat	4 g
Cholesterol	44 mg
Sodium	333 mg
Carbohydrate	43 g
Dietary Fiber	4 g
Protein	20 g
Calcium	51 mg
Iron	3 mg
Vitamin A	153 RE
Vitamin C	26 mg

Linguine with Pesto-Marinara Clam Sauce

Linguine with Pesto-Marinara Clam Sauce

   1 teaspoon vegetable oil
 ¼ cup chopped shallots
   3 cloves garlic, finely chopped
   2 cans (6 ounces each) minced clams
1⅓ cups Marinara Sauce (page 46)
   2 tablespoons prepared pesto sauce
 ¼ teaspoon crushed red pepper
   8 ounces uncooked linguine
 ¼ cup chopped fresh parsley

1. Heat oil in large nonstick saucepan over medium heat until hot. Add shallots and garlic. Cook, covered, 2 minutes.

2. Drain clams; reserve ½ cup juice. Add clams, reserved juice, Marinara Sauce, pesto and red pepper to saucepan. Cook 10 minutes, stirring occasionally.

3. Prepare linguine according to package directions, omitting salt. Drain. Spoon sauce evenly over each serving; top with parsley.

Garnish with lemon slices and additional parsley, if desired.　　*Makes 4 servings*

Dietary Exchanges per Serving:
2½ Starch/Bread, 3 Lean Meat, 2½ Vegetable

NUTRIENTS PER SERVING:

Calories	398
% calories from fat	13
Total Fat	6 g
Saturated Fat	1 g
Cholesterol	58 mg
Sodium	293 mg
Carbohydrate	54 g
Dietary Fiber	4 g
Protein	32 g
Calcium	146 mg
Iron	27 mg
Vitamin A	407 RE
Vitamin C	34 mg

Lemon-Crusted Country Pie

½ cup plus 2 tablespoons all-purpose flour
⅓ cup whole wheat flour
1 teaspoon grated lemon peel
2 tablespoons vegetable oil
3 to 4 tablespoons ice water
   Nonstick cooking spray
1 boneless skinless chicken breast (about 6 ounces), cut into 1-inch pieces
1 cup chopped onion
1 cup chopped celery
1 cup sliced mushrooms
½ cup shredded carrot
1 tablespoon margarine
½ cup ⅓-less-salt chicken broth
½ cup skim milk
½ teaspoon salt
½ teaspoon dried rosemary
¼ teaspoon ground black pepper
1 cup frozen whole kernel corn
1 cup frozen green peas
⅓ cup whole wheat bread crumbs

1. Combine ½ cup all-purpose flour, whole wheat flour and lemon peel in medium bowl. Add oil; blend well. Add water, 1 tablespoon at a time, stirring constantly until soft dough forms. Flatten dough into disc; cover with plastic wrap. Refrigerate 30 minutes.

2. Place dough on lightly floured surface. Roll out dough into 10-inch circle, ⅛ inch thick. Ease dough into 9-inch pie plate. Trim edge; fold edge under. (If excess dough remains, reroll dough and cut out decorative shapes with lightly floured cutters.)

3. Spray large nonstick skillet with cooking spray. Heat over medium heat until hot. Add chicken. Cook and stir 3 minutes. Add onion, celery, mushrooms and carrot. Cook and stir 5 minutes or until chicken is no longer pink. Set aside.

4. Preheat oven to 375°F.

5. Melt margarine in medium saucepan over medium heat. Add remaining 2 tablespoons flour. Cook and stir 3 minutes or until small clumps form. Gradually stir in chicken broth, milk, salt, rosemary and pepper. Cook 6 minutes or until sauce thickens, stirring constantly. Stir in chicken mixture, corn, peas and bread crumbs. Remove saucepan from heat; let stand 15 minutes.

6. Spoon vegetable mixture into prepared crust. (Arrange cut-outs over top of pie, if desired.) Brush crust and cut-outs with additional milk.

7. Bake 50 minutes or until crust is golden brown and filling is set. (If crust browns too much before filling sets, cover crust with strips of aluminum foil.) Let stand 5 minutes before serving. *Makes 4 servings*

Dietary Exchanges per Serving:
2½ Starch/Bread, 1 Lean Meat, 2 Vegetable, 2 Fat

NUTRIENTS PER SERVING:

Calories	372
% calories from fat	29
Total Fat	12 g
Saturated Fat	2 g
Cholesterol	28 mg
Sodium	449 mg
Carbohydrate	47 g
Dietary Fiber	6 g
Protein	19 g
Calcium	97 mg
Iron	3 mg
Vitamin A	540 RE
Vitamin C	13 mg

Mexicali Baked Chicken

Nonstick cooking spray
4 skinless chicken legs (about 2 pounds)
½ cup halved sliced onion
3 cloves garlic, finely chopped
1 cup sliced cooked potato
1 cup no-salt-added vegetable juice cocktail
½ cup halved sliced green bell pepper
½ cup drained canned diced tomatoes
¼ cup ⅓-less-salt chicken broth
2 bay leaves
1 teaspoon paprika
½ teaspoon ground cumin
¼ teaspoon salt
¼ teaspoon ground black pepper

1. Preheat oven to 325°F. Spray large skillet with cooking spray. Heat over medium heat until hot. Add chicken legs, onion and garlic. Cook 5 minutes or until chicken is browned, turning occasionally.

2. Add potato, vegetable juice, bell pepper, tomatoes, chicken broth, bay leaves, paprika, cumin, salt and black pepper to skillet. Cook 5 minutes, stirring occasionally. Spoon into 1-quart casserole.

3. Bake, covered, 45 minutes or until chicken is no longer pink. Remove and discard bay leaves.   *Makes 4 servings*

Dietary Exchanges per Serving:
1 Starch/Bread, 3 Lean Meat, 1 Vegetable

NUTRIENTS PER SERVING:

Calories	258
% calories from fat	27
Total Fat	8 g
Saturated Fat	2 g
Cholesterol	82 mg
Sodium	248 mg
Carbohydrate	21 g
Dietary Fiber	3 g
Protein	26 g
Calcium	41 mg
Iron	3 mg
Vitamin A	128 RE
Vitamin C	49 mg

Spaghetti with Marinara Sauce

1 teaspoon olive oil
¾ cup chopped onion
3 cloves garlic, finely chopped
1 can (16 ounces) no-salt-added tomato sauce
1 can (6 ounces) tomato paste
2 bay leaves
1 teaspoon dried oregano leaves
1 teaspoon dried basil leaves
½ teaspoon dried marjoram leaves
½ teaspoon honey
¼ teaspoon ground black pepper
8 ounces uncooked spaghetti

1. To make Marinara Sauce, heat oil in large saucepan over medium heat until hot. Add onion and garlic. Cook and stir 5 minutes or until onion is tender. Add 2 cups water and remaining ingredients except spaghetti. Bring to a boil, stirring occasionally. Reduce heat to medium-low. Simmer 1 hour, stirring occasionally.

2. Meanwhile, prepare spaghetti according to package directions, omitting salt. Drain.

3. Remove and discard bay leaves. Measure 2 cups sauce; reserve remaining sauce for another use. Spoon evenly over each serving.   *Makes 4 servings*

Dietary Exchanges per Serving:
3 Starch/Bread, 2½ Vegetable

NUTRIENTS PER SERVING:

Calories	289
% calories from fat	<1
Total Fat	2 g
Saturated Fat	<1 g
Cholesterol	0 mg
Sodium	213 mg
Carbohydrate	58 g
Dietary Fiber	3 g
Protein	10 g
Calcium	41 mg
Iron	4 mg
Vitamin A	126 RE
Vitamin C	20 mg

Turkey Jambalaya

1 teaspoon vegetable oil
1 cup chopped onion
1 green bell pepper, chopped
½ cup chopped celery
3 cloves garlic, finely chopped
1¾ cups ⅓-less-salt chicken broth
1 cup chopped seeded tomato
¼ pound cooked ground turkey breast, chopped
¼ pound cooked turkey sausage
3 tablespoons tomato paste
1 bay leaf
1 teaspoon dried basil leaves
¼ teaspoon ground red pepper
1 cup uncooked white rice
¼ cup chopped fresh parsley

Heat oil in large nonstick skillet over medium-high heat until hot. Add onion, bell pepper, celery and garlic. Cook and stir 5 minutes or until vegetables are tender. Add chicken broth, tomato, turkey, turkey sausage, tomato paste, bay leaf, basil and red pepper. Stir in rice. Bring to a boil over high heat, stirring occasionally. Reduce heat to medium-low. Simmer, covered, 20 minutes or until rice is tender and liquid is absorbed. Remove skillet from heat. Remove and discard bay leaf. Top each serving evenly with parsley. Serve immediately.

Makes 4 servings

Dietary Exchanges per Serving:
2½ Starch/Bread, 2 Lean Meat, 2½ Vegetable, ½ Fat

NUTRIENTS PER SERVING:

Calories	416
% calories from fat	18
Total Fat	9 g
Saturated Fat	2 g
Cholesterol	74 mg
Sodium	384 mg
Carbohydrate	51 g
Dietary Fiber	3 g
Protein	28 g
Calcium	84 mg
Iron	5 mg
Vitamin A	306 RE
Vitamin C	44 mg

Shrimp Tostadas

Nonstick cooking spray
1 can (about 15 ounces) kidney beans, rinsed, drained, mashed
1 tablespoon chili powder
2 teaspoons ground cumin
½ teaspoon garlic powder
4 (6-inch) flour tortillas
3 cups shredded lettuce leaves
8 ounces cooked medium shrimp
2 cups Spicy Salsa, (page 21)
4 tablespoons plain nonfat yogurt

1. Preheat oven to 375°F.

2. Spray medium nonstick skillet with cooking spray. Heat over medium heat until hot. Add beans, chili powder, cumin and garlic powder. Cook and stir 5 minutes or until heated through. Reduce heat to low.

3. Place tortillas on baking sheet. Bake 3 to 4 minutes or until tortillas are crisp.

4. Spread bean mixture evenly over tortillas. Top tortillas evenly with lettuce and shrimp.

Spoon salsa evenly over tortillas; top with dollops of yogurt. Serve immediately.

Makes 4 servings

Dietary Exchanges per Serving:
2½ Starch/Bread, 2 Lean Meat, 1 Vegetable

NUTRIENTS PER SERVING:

Calories	303
% calories from fat	11
Total Fat	4 g
Saturated Fat	1 g
Cholesterol	111 mg
Sodium	392 mg
Carbohydrate	48 g
Dietary Fiber	10 g
Protein	26 g
Calcium	88 mg
Iron	3 mg
Vitamin A	260 RE
Vitamin C	27 mg

Fettuccine Alfredo

Fettuccine Alfredo

2 teaspoons margarine
3 cloves garlic, finely chopped
4½ teaspoons all-purpose flour
1½ cups skim milk
½ cup grated Parmesan cheese
3½ teaspoons Neufchâtel cheese
¼ teaspoon ground white pepper
4 ounces hot, cooked fettuccine
¼ cup chopped fresh parsley

1. Melt margarine in medium saucepan over medium heat. Add garlic. Cook and stir 1 minute. Stir in flour. Cook and stir 2 minutes or until small clumps form. Gradually stir in milk. Cook 6 minutes or until sauce thickens, stirring constantly. Stir in cheeses and pepper. Cook 2 minutes or until cheeses melt, stirring constantly.

2. Spoon sauce over fettuccine; toss to coat. Sprinkle parsley evenly over each serving. Garnish as desired.   *Makes 4 servings*

Dietary Exchanges per Serving:
2 Starch/Bread, 1 Lean Meat, 1 Fat

NUTRIENTS PER SERVING:

Calories	242
% calories from fat	33
Total Fat	9 g
Saturated Fat	4 g
Cholesterol	18 mg
Sodium	344 mg
Carbohydrate	27 g
Dietary Fiber	1 g
Protein	14 g
Calcium	307 mg
Iron	1 mg
Vitamin A	160 RE
Vitamin C	7 mg

Beef & Vegetable Stir-Fry

½ cup ⅓-less-salt beef broth
3 tablespoons reduced sodium soy
    sauce
2 teaspoons cornstarch
1 teaspoon sugar
½ teaspoon ground ginger
½ teaspoon garlic powder
½ teaspoon Oriental sesame oil
¼ teaspoon salt
¼ teaspoon ground black pepper
1 teaspoon vegetable oil
½ pound beef flank steak, cut
    diagonally into 1-inch slices
2 green bell peppers, thinly sliced
1 cup tomato wedges
8 green onions, cut into 1-inch pieces
4 cups hot, cooked white rice (optional)

1. Combine beef broth, soy sauce,
cornstarch, sugar, ginger, garlic powder,
sesame oil, salt and black pepper in medium
bowl; whisk until blended.

2. Heat vegetable oil in wok or nonstick
skillet until hot. Add beef; stir-fry 3 minutes
or until beef is browned. Add bell peppers,
tomato and onions; stir-fry 2 minutes or until
vegetables are crisp-tender.

3. Stir beef broth mixture; add to wok. Cook
and stir 3 minutes or until sauce boils and
thickens.

4. Serve beef mixture over hot, cooked
white rice, if desired.   *Makes 4 servings*

Dietary Exchanges per Serving:
2½ Starch/Bread, 2 Lean Meat, 2 Vegetable

NUTRIENTS PER SERVING:

Calories	357
% calories from fat	15
Total Fat	6 g
Saturated Fat	2 g
Cholesterol	23 mg
Sodium	614 mg
Carbohydrate	54 g
Dietary Fiber	2 g
Protein	19 g
Calcium	35 mg
Iron	4 mg
Vitamin A	108 RE
Vitamin C	48 mg

Penne Pasta with Shrimp

1 tablespoon reduced calorie margarine
½ cup chopped green onions
3 cloves garlic, finely chopped
1 shallot, finely chopped
1 tablespoon all-purpose flour
1 cup ⅓-less-salt chicken broth
10 ounces medium shrimp, peeled and
    deveined
¾ cup shredded carrots
⅛ teaspoon lemon pepper seasoning
1 package (10 ounces) frozen chopped
    spinach, thawed
8 ounces hot, cooked penne pasta

1. Melt margarine in medium nonstick skillet
over medium-high heat. Add onions, garlic
and shallot. Cook and stir 5 minutes or until
garlic is tender. Stir in flour. Cook and stir 2
minutes or until small clumps form.
Gradually stir in chicken broth. Cook and stir
until sauce boils and thickens.

2. Add shrimp, carrots and lemon pepper to
skillet. Simmer 3 minutes. Add spinach;
simmer 2 minutes or until shrimp are
opaque, turning occasionally. Serve shrimp
and vegetable mixture over pasta.
    Makes 4 servings

Dietary Exchanges per Serving:
2 Starch/Bread, 2 Lean Meat, 2 Vegetable

NUTRIENTS PER SERVING:

Calories	308
% calories from fat	12
Total Fat	4 g
Saturated Fat	1 g
Cholesterol	109 mg
Sodium	319 mg
Carbohydrate	46 g
Dietary Fiber	5 g
Protein	23 g
Calcium	148 mg
Iron	5 mg
Vitamin A	1,279 RE
Vitamin C	17 mg

Tamale Pie

BISCUIT TOPPING

½ **cup white or yellow cornmeal**
½ **cup buttermilk**
⅓ **cup all-purpose flour**
1 **egg white, slightly beaten**
1 **tablespoon sugar**
½ **jalapeño pepper, seeded, chopped**
1 **teaspoon baking powder**

FILLING

Nonstick cooking spray
1 **green bell pepper, chopped**
¾ **cup chopped green onions**
2 **cloves garlic, finely chopped**
1½ **cups canned crushed tomatoes**
1 **can (about 15 ounces) pinto beans, rinsed and drained**
¼ **pound cooked ground turkey breast**
2 **teaspoons chili powder**
1 **teaspoon ground cumin**
¼ **teaspoon ground black pepper**

1. Preheat oven to 425°F. Spray 9-inch pie plate with nonstick cooking spray; set aside.

2. For topping, combine all topping ingredients in large bowl until well blended; set aside.

3. For filling, spray large nonstick skillet with cooking spray. Heat over medium heat until hot. Add bell pepper, onions and garlic.

Cook and stir 5 minutes or until vegetables are tender. Add tomatoes, beans, turkey, chili powder, cumin and black pepper. Cook and stir 5 minutes or until heated through.

4. Spoon vegetable mixture into prepared pie plate. Drop heaping tablespoonfuls topping around outer edge of filling; flatten with back of spoon to form biscuits.

5. Bake 25 minutes or until biscuits are golden brown. Let stand 5 minutes before serving. *Makes 4 servings*

Dietary Exchanges per Serving:
2½ Starch/Bread, 1 Lean Meat, 1 Vegetable

NUTRIENTS PER SERVING:

Calories	274
% calories from fat	13
Total Fat	4 g
Saturated Fat	1 g
Cholesterol	12 mg
Sodium	750 mg
Carbohydrate	47 g
Dietary Fiber	4 g
Protein	14 g
Calcium	140 mg
Iron	5 mg
Vitamin A	199 RE
Vitamin C	45 mg

Bow Tie Pasta with Puttanesca Sauce

1 **teaspoon olive oil**
3 **cloves garlic, finely chopped**
1 **can (28 ounces) crushed Italian-style tomatoes, undrained**
1 **can (9 ounces) water-packed white tuna, rinsed and drained**
¼ **cup sliced black olives**
¼ **teaspoon crushed red pepper**
¼ **teaspoon ground black pepper**
8 **ounces hot, cooked bow tie pasta**

1. Heat oil in large saucepan over medium-high heat until hot. Add garlic. Cook and stir 3 minutes. Stir in remaining ingredients except pasta. Reduce heat to medium-low. Simmer 5 minutes, stirring occasionally.

2. Spoon sauce evenly over each serving. Serve immediately. *Makes 4 servings*

Dietary Exchanges per Serving:
2½ Starch/Bread, 2 Lean Meat, 2 Vegetable

NUTRIENTS PER SERVING:

Calories	351
% calories from fat	17
Total Fat	7 g
Saturated Fat	1 g
Cholesterol	19 mg
Sodium	825 mg
Carbohydrate	47 g
Dietary Fiber	4 g
Protein	26 g
Calcium	80 mg
Iron	4 mg
Vitamin A	143 RE
Vitamin C	31 mg

Rio Grande Bean Enchiladas

Rio Grande Bean Enchiladas

3 teaspoons olive oil, divided
2 cups chopped onions, divided
1 can (14½ ounces) crushed tomatoes, undrained
1 can (6 ounces) tomato paste
2 tablespoons chili powder
1 tablespoon prepared green salsa
2 teaspoons ground cumin, divided
1 teaspoon sugar
⅛ teaspoon ground black pepper
2 cloves garlic, finely chopped
1 can (about 15 ounces) black beans, rinsed, drained, mashed
1 cup plain nonfat yogurt
8 (6-inch) corn tortillas

1. Heat 2 teaspoons oil in large saucepan over medium-high heat until hot. Add 1 cup onions. Cook and stir 5 minutes or until tender. Stir in tomatoes, tomato paste, chili powder, salsa, 1 teaspoon cumin, sugar and pepper. Reduce heat to medium-low. Simmer 30 minutes.

2. Heat remaining 1 teaspoon oil in large skillet over medium-high heat until hot. Add remaining 1 cup onions, remaining 1 teaspoon cumin and garlic. Cook and stir 5 minutes or until onions are tender. Stir in beans. Cook 5 minutes or until heated through, stirring occasionally. Remove skillet from heat. Stir in yogurt.

3. Preheat oven to 375°F. Spoon bean mixture evenly down centers of tortillas. Roll up tortillas; place in medium baking dish. Pour sauce over tortillas.

4. Bake 20 minutes. Serve with dollops of nonfat sour cream and cilantro, if desired. Garnish as desired. *Makes 4 servings*

Dietary Exchanges per Serving:
3 Starch/Bread, 4 Vegetable, 1½ Fat

NUTRIENTS PER SERVING:

Calories	365
% calories from fat	17
Total Fat	7 g
Saturated Fat	1 g
Cholesterol	1 mg
Sodium	1,050 mg
Carbohydrate	69 g
Dietary Fiber	11 g
Protein	19 g
Calcium	282 mg
Iron	4 mg
Vitamin A	315 RE
Vitamin C	44 mg

Turkey Burger

Turkey Burgers

1 pound ground turkey breast
1 cup whole wheat bread crumbs
1 egg white
½ teaspoon dried sage leaves
½ teaspoon dried marjoram leaves
¼ teaspoon salt
¼ teaspoon ground black pepper
1 teaspoon vegetable oil
4 whole grain sandwich rolls, split in half
4 tablespoons Cowpoke Barbecue Sauce (page 54)*

*Or substitute prepared barbecue sauce.

1. Combine turkey, bread crumbs, egg white, sage, marjoram, salt and pepper in large bowl until well blended. Shape into 4 patties.

2. Heat oil in large nonstick skillet over medium-high heat until hot. Add patties. Cook 10 minutes or until patties are no longer pink in center, turning once.

3. Place one patty on bottom half of each roll. Spoon 1 tablespoon Cowpoke Barbecue Sauce over top of each burger. Place tops of rolls over burgers. Serve with lettuce and tomato, if desired. Garnish with carrot slices, if desired. Serve immediately.

Makes 4 burgers

Dietary Exchanges per Serving:
2 Starch/Bread, 3 Lean Meat

NUTRIENTS PER SERVING:

Calories	319
% calories from fat	17
Total Fat	6 g
Saturated Fat	1 g
Cholesterol	41 mg
Sodium	669 mg
Carbohydrate	40 g
Dietary Fiber	2 g
Protein	26 g
Calcium	116 mg
Iron	3 mg
Vitamin A	20 RE
Vitamin C	4 mg

Ginger-Crab Stir-Fry

Hot Orange Sauce (recipe follows)
- 1 teaspoon vegetable oil
- 1 cup sliced onion
- 3 cloves garlic, finely chopped
- ½ teaspoon ground ginger
- 1 package (6 ounces) frozen snow peas
- 1 cup drained jarred straw mushrooms
- 1 can (7½ ounces) baby corn, rinsed and drained
- 16 ounces imitation crab sticks, thinly sliced
- 2 cups hot, cooked white rice

1. Prepare Hot Orange Sauce; set aside.

2. Heat oil in wok or large nonstick skillet until hot. Add onion, garlic and ginger; stir-fry 30 seconds. Add snow peas, mushrooms and corn; stir-fry 2 minutes. Add crab slices and Hot Orange Sauce; cook and stir 1 minute or until heated through.

3. Serve crab mixture over rice.

Makes 4 servings

Hot Orange Sauce

- ¼ cup orange juice
- 3 tablespoons reduced sodium soy sauce
- 1 tablespoon cider vinegar
- ½ teaspoon ground ginger
- ½ teaspoon Oriental sesame oil
- ¼ teaspoon crushed red pepper

Combine all ingredients in small bowl; whisk until well blended.

Dietary Exchanges per Serving:
2½ Starch/Bread, 2 Lean Meat, 3 Vegetable

NUTRIENTS PER SERVING:

Calories	359
% calories from fat	11
Total Fat	4 g
Saturated Fat	1 g
Cholesterol	23 mg
Sodium	1,796 mg
Carbohydrate	61 g
Dietary Fiber	5 g
Protein	22 g
Calcium	76 mg
Iron	3 mg
Vitamin A	45 RE
Vitamin C	45 mg

Health Note: Recent studies have shown that garlic may play a role in the prevention of heart disease. Results indicate that a clove a day may lower levels of bad cholesterol (LDL), may help prevent the formation of blood clots that lead to heart attacks and strokes, and may aid in lowering high blood pressure levels.

Chicken Fajitas with Cowpoke Barbecue Sauce

1 cup Cowpoke Barbecue Sauce (recipe follows), divided
Nonstick cooking spray
10 ounces boneless skinless chicken breasts, cut lengthwise into 1 × ½-inch pieces
2 green or red bell peppers, thinly sliced
1 cup sliced onion
2 cups tomato wedges
4 (6-inch) warm flour tortillas

1. Prepare Cowpoke Barbecue Sauce.

2. Spray large nonstick skillet with cooking spray. Heat over medium-high heat until hot. Brush chicken with ¼ cup barbecue sauce. Add to skillet. Cook and stir 3 minutes or until chicken is browned. Add peppers and onion. Cook and stir 3 minutes or until vegetables are crisp-tender and chicken is no longer pink. Add tomatoes. Cook 2 minutes or until heated through, stirring occasionally.

3. Serve with warm flour tortillas and remaining ¾ cup Cowpoke Barbecue Sauce. Garnish as desired.   *Makes 4 servings*

Cowpoke Barbecue Sauce

1 teaspoon vegetable oil
¾ cup chopped green onions
3 cloves garlic, finely chopped
1 can (14½ ounces) crushed tomatoes
½ cup ketchup
¼ cup orange juice
2 tablespoons cider vinegar
2 teaspoons chili sauce
Dash Worcestershire sauce

Heat oil in large nonstick saucepan over medium heat until hot. Add onions and garlic. Cook and stir 5 minutes or until onions are tender. Stir in tomatoes with liquid, ketchup, ¼ cup water, orange juice, vinegar, chili sauce and Worcestershire sauce. Reduce heat to medium-low. Cook 15 minutes, stirring occasionally.

Makes 2 cups

Dietary Exchanges per Serving:
1½ Starch/Bread, 2 Lean Meat, 2½ Vegetable

NUTRIENTS PER SERVING:

Calories	310
% calories from fat	18
Total Fat	6 g
Saturated Fat	1 g
Cholesterol	36 mg
Sodium	736 mg
Carbohydrate	47 g
Dietary Fiber	4 g
Protein	20 g
Calcium	104 mg
Iron	3 mg
Vitamin A	259 RE
Vitamin C	90 mg

Health Note: Nearly 50 percent of adults with high blood pressure do not experience a reduction in blood pressure levels when the amount of sodium in their diets is reduced. Elevated levels are much more responsive to calcium-rich meals, leading many researchers to believe that good-for-your-bones calcium plays a major role in the maintenance of near normal blood pressure levels.

Chicken Fajitas with Cowpoke Barbecue Sauce

Pasta Primavera

4 ounces uncooked spinach fettuccine
1 cup plain nonfat yogurt
¼ cup packed fresh parsley
¼ cup packed fresh chives
½ teaspoon salt
¼ teaspoon ground black pepper
1 teaspoon margarine
1 teaspoon vegetable oil
½ pound fresh or thawed frozen
    asparagus, cut diagonally into
    ½-inch pieces
1 cup thinly sliced carrots
1 cup thawed frozen green peas
¾ cup thawed frozen cut green beans
3 cloves garlic, finely chopped
2 tablespoons grated Parmesan cheese

1. Cook fettuccine according to package directions, omitting salt. Drain fettuccine. Set aside.

2. In food processor or blender combine yogurt, parsley, chives, salt and pepper; process until smooth.

3. Heat margarine and oil in medium saucepan over medium heat until hot. Add asparagus, carrots, peas, beans and garlic. Cook and stir 8 minutes or until vegetables are tender. Stir in pasta and yogurt mixture. Cook 3 minutes or until heated through, stirring occasionally. Sprinkle cheese evenly over each serving. Serve immediately.

Makes 4 servings

Dietary Exchanges per Serving:
3 Starch/Bread, ½ Milk, 1½ Vegetable, ½ Fat

NUTRIENTS PER SERVING:

Calories	339
% calories from fat	13
Total Fat	5 g
Saturated Fat	2 g
Cholesterol	6 mg
Sodium	422 mg
Carbohydrate	58 g
Dietary Fiber	3 g
Protein	16 g
Calcium	253 mg
Iron	3 mg
Vitamin A	893 RE
Vitamin C	42 mg

Oriental Stir-Fry

½ cup ⅓-less-salt chicken broth
3 tablespoons reduced sodium soy
    sauce
2 tablespoons cornstarch
2 tablespoons rice wine vinegar
¼ teaspoon ground black pepper
1 teaspoon peanut oil
½ pound coarsely chopped leeks
3 cloves garlic, finely chopped
¼ teaspoon ground ginger
1 cup broccoli flowerets
1 cup thinly sliced carrots
1 large Granny Smith apple, peeled,
    cored, cut into 1-inch pieces
3 cups hot, cooked white rice
¼ cup peanuts, coarsely chopped

1. Combine chicken broth, soy sauce, cornstarch, vinegar and pepper in small bowl; whisk until well blended.

2. Heat oil in wok until hot. Add leeks, garlic and ginger; stir-fry 3 minutes. Add broccoli, carrots and apple; stir-fry 3 minutes. Stir soy sauce mixture; add to wok. Cook and stir until sauce boils and thickens. Stir in rice and peanuts. Serve immediately

Makes 4 servings

Dietary Exchanges per Serving:
2½ Starch/Bread, 2 Vegetable, ½ Fruit, 1 Fat

NUTRIENTS PER SERVING:

Calories	317
% calories from fat	18
Total Fat	6 g
Saturated Fat	1 g
Cholesterol	0 mg
Sodium	467 mg
Carbohydrate	58 g
Dietary Fiber	4 g
Protein	9 g
Calcium	80 mg
Iron	4 mg
Vitamin A	815 RE
Vitamin C	32 mg

Pork with Couscous & Root Vegetables

Pork with Couscous & Root Vegetables

1 teaspoon vegetable oil
½ pound pork tenderloin, thinly sliced
2 sweet potatoes, peeled, chopped
2 medium turnips, peeled, chopped
1 carrot, sliced
3 cloves garlic, finely chopped
1 can (about 15 ounces) garbanzo beans (chick-peas), rinsed and drained
1 cup ⅓-less-salt vegetable broth
½ cup pitted prunes, cut into thirds
1 teaspoon ground cumin
½ teaspoon ground cinnamon
¼ teaspoon ground allspice
¼ teaspoon ground nutmeg
¼ teaspoon ground black pepper
1 cup uncooked quick-cooking couscous, cooked
2 tablespoons dried currants

1. Heat oil in large nonstick skillet over medium-high heat until hot. Add pork, sweet potatoes, turnips, carrot and garlic. Cook and stir 5 minutes. Stir in beans, vegetable broth, prunes, cumin, cinnamon, allspice, nutmeg and pepper. Cover; bring to a boil over high heat. Reduce heat to medium-low. Simmer 30 minutes.

2. Serve pork and vegetables over couscous. Top each serving evenly with currants. Garnish with sprigs of thyme, if desired.   *Makes 4 servings*

Dietary Exchanges per Serving:
4 Starch/Bread, 2 Lean Meat, 1 Fruit, 2 Vegetable

NUTRIENTS PER SERVING:

Calories	508
% calories from fat	11
Total Fat	6 g
Saturated Fat	1 g
Cholesterol	30 mg
Sodium	500 mg
Carbohydrate	88 g
Dietary Fiber	17 g
Protein	26 g
Calcium	117 mg
Iron	5 mg
Vitamin A	1,793 RE
Vitamin C	28 mg

Mexican Pilaf Casserole

1 teaspoon vegetable oil
½ cup uncooked brown rice
½ cup chopped onion
½ green or red bell pepper, chopped
3 cloves garlic, finely chopped
1 cup ⅓-less-salt chicken broth
½ cup rinsed, drained canned black
    beans, cooked
1 teaspoon dried oregano leaves
½ teaspoon chili powder
¼ teaspoon ground cumin
¼ teaspoon ground black pepper

1. Preheat oven to 400°F. Spray 1-quart casserole with nonstick cooking spray; set aside.

2. Heat oil in large nonstick skillet over medium heat until hot. Add rice, onion, bell pepper and garlic. Cook and stir 3 minutes or until rice is browned. Stir in chicken broth, beans, oregano, chili powder, cumin and black pepper. Bring to a boil over high heat, stirring occasionally. Remove skillet from heat.

3. Spoon rice mixture into prepared casserole; cover. Bake 40 minutes or until rice is tender and chicken broth is absorbed. Let stand 10 minutes before serving.
Makes 2 servings

Dietary Exchanges per Serving:
3 Starch/Bread, 3 Vegetable, 1½ Fat

NUTRIENTS PER SERVING:

Calories	359
% calories from fat	17
Total Fat	7 g
Saturated Fat	1 g
Cholesterol	29 mg
Sodium	178 mg
Carbohydrate	52 g
Dietary Fiber	7 g
Protein	18 g
Calcium	68 mg
Iron	3 mg
Vitamin A	268 RE
Vitamin C	23 mg

Broccoli-Topped Baked Potatoes

4 medium baking potatoes, washed
1 teaspoon olive oil
½ pound broccoli flowerets
2 green onions, finely chopped
3 cloves garlic, finely chopped
1 tablespoon margarine
2 teaspoons all-purpose flour
1 cup plain nonfat yogurt
¼ cup cholesterol free egg substitute
¼ teaspoon salt
⅛ teaspoon ground white pepper

1. Prick potatoes with fork; place in microwave on paper towels. Microwave at HIGH 10 minutes, or until tender, turning once. Let stand 10 minutes or until cool enough to handle.

2. Meanwhile, heat oil in medium skillet over medium-high heat until hot. Add broccoli, onions and garlic. Cook and stir 5 minutes or until vegetables are tender. Remove skillet from heat.

3. Melt margarine in medium saucepan over low heat. Add flour. Cook and stir 3 minutes or until small clumps form. Whisk in remaining ingredients. Cook 1 minute, stirring constantly. Remove saucepan from heat. Add broccoli mixture; toss to coat.

4. Cut potatoes lengthwise in half. Spoon broccoli mixture evenly over potatoes. Serve immediately. *Makes 4 servings*

Dietary Exchanges per Serving:
3 Starch/Bread, 2 Vegetable, 1 Fat

NUTRIENTS PER SERVING:

Calories	318
% calories from fat	12
Total Fat	5 g
Saturated Fat	<1 g
Cholesterol	0 mg
Sodium	258 mg
Carbohydrate	60 g
Dietary Fiber	7 g
Protein	11 g
Calcium	172 mg
Iron	4 mg
Vitamin A	196 RE
Vitamin C	71 mg

Shrimp and Pineapple Kabobs

½ cup pineapple juice
¼ teaspoon garlic powder
8 ounces medium shrimp, peeled and deveined
12 chunks canned pineapple
1 green bell pepper, cut into 1-inch pieces
¼ cup prepared chili sauce

1. To prevent sticking, spray grill with nonstick cooking spray. Prepare coals for grilling.

2. Combine pineapple juice and garlic powder in large resealable plastic food storage bag. Add shrimp. Seal bag; toss to coat. Marinate in refrigerator 30 minutes. Drain shrimp; discard marinade.

3. Alternately thread pineapple, peppers and shrimp onto 4 (10-inch) skewers. (If using bamboo skewers, soak them in water 20 minutes before using to prevent them from burning.) Brush chili sauce over kabobs.

4. Place kabobs on grill, 4 inches from hot coals. Grill 5 minutes or until shrimp are opaque, turning once and basting with chili sauce. Serve immediately.

Makes 4 servings

Dietary Exchanges per Serving:
1 Lean Meat, ½ Fruit, 1 Vegetable

NUTRIENTS PER SERVING:

Calories	100
% calories from fat	7
Total Fat	<1 g
Saturated Fat	<1 g
Cholesterol	87 mg
Sodium	302 mg
Carbohydrate	14 g
Dietary Fiber	1 g
Protein	10 g
Calcium	30 mg
Iron	2 mg
Vitamin A	94 RE
Vitamin C	61 mg

Bow Tie Pasta with Caramelized Onions

½ cup dry-pack sun-dried tomatoes
    Nonstick cooking spray
2 cups sliced onions
3 cloves garlic, finely chopped
2½ cups ⅓-less-salt chicken broth
1 tablespoon cornstarch
1 package (10 ounces) frozen chopped spinach, thawed
2 cups uncooked bow tie pasta, cooked
2 tablespoons grated Parmesan cheese

1. Combine 1 cup boiling water and tomatoes in small bowl. Let stand 30 minutes. Drain tomatoes; discard liquid. Coarsely chop.

2. Spray large nonstick skillet with cooking spray. Heat over medium heat until hot. Add onions and garlic; cook, covered, 10 minutes.

3. Combine chicken broth and cornstarch in small bowl until well blended. Add to skillet. Cook until mixture boils and thickens, stirring occasionally. Add tomatoes, spinach and pasta. Cook 3 minutes or until heated through.

4. Sprinkle cheese evenly over each serving.

Makes 6 servings

Dietary Exchanges per Serving:
2 Starch/Bread, 1½ Vegetable, ½ Fat

NUTRIENTS PER SERVING:

Calories	202
% calories from fat	10
Total Fat	2 g
Saturated Fat	1 g
Cholesterol	2 mg
Sodium	233 mg
Carbohydrate	37 g
Dietary Fiber	4 g
Protein	11 g
Calcium	124 mg
Iron	2 mg
Vitamin A	621 RE
Vitamin C	15 mg

Stir-Fried Pork Lo Mein

Stir-Fried Pork Lo Mein

Nonstick cooking spray
6 green onions, cut into 1-inch pieces
½ teaspoon garlic powder
½ teaspoon ground ginger
6 ounces pork loin roast, thinly sliced
3 cups shredded green cabbage
½ cup shredded carrots
½ cup trimmed snow peas
½ cup ⅓-less-salt chicken broth
2 teaspoons cornstarch
2 tablespoons hoisin sauce (optional)
1 tablespoon reduced sodium soy sauce
8 ounces cooked linguine

1. Spray wok with cooking spray. Heat over medium heat until hot. Add onions, garlic powder and ginger; stir-fry 30 seconds. Add pork; stir-fry 2 minutes or until pork is no longer pink. Add vegetables; stir-fry 3 minutes or until vegetables are crisp-tender.

2. Combine chicken broth, cornstarch, hoisin sauce and soy sauce in small bowl; blend well. Add to wok. Cook and stir until mixture boils and thickens. Stir in pasta; cook until heated through. Garnish as desired.

Makes 4 servings

Dietary Exchanges per Serving:
3 Starch/Bread, 1 Lean Meat, 1½ Vegetable

NUTRIENTS PER SERVING:

Calories	310
% calories from fat	13
Total Fat	4 g
Saturated Fat	1 g
Cholesterol	25 mg
Sodium	228 mg
Carbohydrate	48 g
Dietary Fiber	4 g
Protein	20 g
Calcium	66 mg
Iron	3 mg
Vitamin A	445 RE
Vitamin C	48 mg

Paella

Nonstick cooking spray
10 ounces boneless skinless chicken breasts
1 teaspoon vegetable oil
½ cup uncooked white rice
4 cloves garlic, finely chopped
½ cup sliced onion
½ cup sliced green bell pepper
1 cup ⅓-less salt chicken broth
½ teaspoon ground turmeric
¼ teaspoon salt
¼ teaspoon paprika
¼ teaspoon ground black pepper
½ cup frozen green peas
½ cup drained canned diced tomatoes
8 ounces medium shrimp, peeled and deveined

1. Preheat oven to 350°F. Spray large skillet with cooking spray; heat over medium-high heat until hot. Add chicken. Cook 10 minutes or until chicken is no longer pink in center, turning once. Remove chicken from skillet. Cool 10 minutes or until cool enough to handle. Cut into 1-inch pieces.

2. Heat oil in large ovenproof skillet or paella pan over medium heat until hot. Add rice and garlic. Cook 5 minutes or until rice is browned, stirring occasionally. Add onion and bell pepper. Stir in chicken broth, turmeric, salt, paprika and black pepper. Stir in peas and tomatoes. Place chicken and shrimp over top of rice mixture.

3. Bake 20 to 30 minutes or until heated through. Let stand 5 minutes before serving.
Makes 4 servings

Dietary Exchanges per Serving:
1½ Starch/Bread, 3 Lean Meat, 1 Vegetable

NUTRIENTS PER SERVING:

Calories	258
% calories from fat	14
Total Fat	4 g
Saturated Fat	1 g
Cholesterol	123 mg
Sodium	371 mg
Carbohydrate	28 g
Dietary Fiber	2 g
Protein	27 g
Calcium	51 mg
Iron	4 mg
Vitamin A	95 RE
Vitamin C	36 mg

Southwestern Chili

1 teaspoon vegetable oil
1 pound lean beef sirloin steak, chopped
1 cup chopped onion
4 cloves garlic, finely chopped
1 cup rinsed, drained canned kidney beans, ¼ cup liquid reserved
1 cup drained canned diced tomatoes, ¼ cup liquid reserved
3 tablespoons ketchup
2 teaspoons chili powder
1½ teaspoons ground cumin
½ teaspoon dried oregano leaves
¼ teaspoon ground red pepper

1. Heat oil in large skillet over medium heat until hot. Add steak, onion and garlic. Cook and stir 5 minutes or until steak is browned.

2. Add beans with reserved liquid, tomatoes with reserved liquid, ketchup and seasonings to skillet. Reduce heat to medium-low. Simmer, 30 minutes, stirring occasionally.
Makes 4 servings

Dietary Exchanges per Serving:
1 Starch/Bread, 3 Lean Meat, 1 Vegetable

NUTRIENTS PER SERVING:

Calories	236
% calories from fat	21
Total Fat	6 g
Saturated Fat	2 g
Cholesterol	55 mg
Sodium	533 mg
Carbohydrate	21 g
Dietary Fiber	5 g
Protein	26 g
Calcium	66 mg
Iron	4 mg
Vitamin A	101 RE
Vitamin C	16 mg

Versatile Vegetables & Sides

Pick-of-the-crop vegetables star in this magnificent chapter. Discover your low fat, high fiber favorites tucked into scrumptious sides or packed into memorable main dishes.

Potatoes au Gratin

- 1 pound baking potatoes
- 4 teaspoons reduced calorie margarine
- 4 teaspoons all-purpose flour
- 1¼ cups skim milk
- ¼ teaspoon ground nutmeg
- ¼ teaspoon paprika
  Pinch ground white pepper
- ½ cup thinly sliced red onion, divided
- ⅓ cup whole wheat bread crumbs
- 1 tablespoon finely chopped red onion
- 1 tablespoon grated Parmesan cheese

1. Preheat oven to 350°F. Spray 4- or 6-cup casserole with nonstick cooking spray.

2. Place potatoes in large saucepan; add water to cover. Bring to a boil over high heat. Boil 12 minutes or until potatoes are tender. Drain potatoes; discard liquid. Let potatoes stand 10 minutes or until cool enough to handle.

3. Melt margarine in small saucepan over medium heat. Add flour. Cook and stir 3 minutes or until small clumps form. Gradually whisk in milk. Cook 8 minutes or until sauce thickens, stirring constantly. Remove saucepan from heat. Stir in nutmeg, paprika and pepper.

4. Cut potatoes into thin slices. Arrange half of potato slices in prepared casserole. Sprinkle half of onion slices over potatoes. Repeat layers. Spoon sauce over potato mixture. Combine bread crumbs, finely chopped red onion and cheese in small bowl. Sprinkle mixture evenly over sauce.

5. Bake 20 minutes. Let stand 5 minutes before serving. Garnish as desired.

Makes 4 servings

Dietary Exchanges per Serving:
2 Starch/Bread, ½ Vegetable, ½ Fat

NUTRIENTS PER SERVING:

Calories	178
% calories from fat	14
Total Fat	3 g
Saturated Fat	1 g
Cholesterol	2 mg
Sodium	144 mg
Carbohydrate	33 g
Dietary Fiber	2 g
Protein	6 g
Calcium	135 mg
Iron	1 mg
Vitamin A	103 RE
Vitamin C	10 mg

Broccoli with Creamy Lemon Sauce

Broccoli with Creamy Lemon Sauce

  2 tablespoons fat free mayonnaise
4½ teaspoons low fat sour cream
  1 tablespoon skim milk
  1 to 1½ teaspoons lemon juice
 ⅛ teaspoon ground turmeric
1¼ cups hot, cooked broccoli flowerets

1. Combine mayonnaise, sour cream, milk, lemon juice and turmeric in top of double boiler. Cook 5 minutes over medium heat or until heated through, stirring constantly.

2. Serve sauce over hot, cooked broccoli.
Makes 2 servings

Dietary Exchanges per Serving:
2 Vegetable

NUTRIENTS PER SERVING:

Calories	44
% calories from fat	18
Total Fat	1 g
Saturated Fat	<1 g
Cholesterol	4 mg
Sodium	216 mg
Carbohydrate	7 g
Dietary Fiber	2 g
Protein	2 g
Calcium	50 mg
Iron	1 mg
Vitamin A	132 RE
Vitamin C	53 mg

Corn Soufflé

1 tablespoon reduced calorie margarine
1 green onion, finely chopped
1 tablespoon all-purpose flour
⅓ cup evaporated skim milk
¾ cup frozen whole kernel corn, thawed
¼ cup cholesterol free egg substitute
   Pinch ground white pepper
   Pinch ground nutmeg
2 egg whites
½ teaspoon cream of tartar
1 tablespoon grated Parmesan cheese

1. Preheat oven to 375°F. Spray 2-cup soufflé dish with nonstick cooking spray.

2. Melt margarine in medium nonstick skillet over medium heat. Add onion. Cook and stir 2 minutes. Stir in flour. Cook and stir 3 minutes or until small clumps form. Gradually stir in milk with wire whisk. Bring to a boil over high heat, stirring constantly. Combine milk mixture, corn, egg substitute, pepper and nutmeg in medium bowl.

3. With clean beaters, beat egg whites in small bowl with electric mixer at medium speed until soft peaks form. Add cream of tartar. Beat at high speed until stiff peaks form.

4. Gently fold egg whites into corn mixture. Gently spoon mixture into prepared dish. Sprinkle cheese evenly over top of corn mixture.

5. Bake 17 minutes or until knife inserted in center comes out clean. Serve immediately.
Makes 2 servings

Dietary Exchanges per Serving:
1 Starch/Bread, 1 Lean Meat, ½ Milk

NUTRIENTS PER SERVING:

Calories	166
% calories from fat	21
Total Fat	4 g
Saturated Fat	1 g
Cholesterol	4 mg
Sodium	262 mg
Carbohydrate	22 g
Dietary Fiber	1 g
Protein	12 g
Calcium	179 mg
Iron	1 mg
Vitamin A	255 RE
Vitamin C	3 mg

French-Style Green Peas

8 pearl onions
2 small heads Boston lettuce, washed and torn
1½ cups frozen baby green peas, thawed
2 teaspoons finely chopped fresh parsley
⅛ teaspoon dried chervil leaves
   Pinch ground white pepper
1 tablespoon reduced calorie margarine
½ teaspoon sugar

1. Combine onions and ½ cup water in small saucepan. Bring to a boil over high heat. Reduce heat to medium-low. Simmer 15 minutes or until onions are tender. Drain.

2. Combine onions, lettuce, peas, parsley, chervil and pepper in medium saucepan. Bring to a simmer over medium-low heat. Cook 6 minutes or until peas are tender. Stir in margarine and sugar; toss to combine. Serve immediately. *Makes 2 servings*

Dietary Exchanges per Serving:
1½ Starch/Bread, ½ Vegetable, ½ Fat

NUTRIENTS PER SERVING:

Calories	151
% calories from fat	20
Total Fat	3 g
Saturated Fat	1 g
Cholesterol	0 mg
Sodium	183 mg
Carbohydrate	24 g
Dietary Fiber	6 g
Protein	8 g
Calcium	88 mg
Iron	3 mg
Vitamin A	293 RE
Vitamin C	38 mg

Spicy Home Fries

2½ teaspoons vegetable oil
1 clove garlic, finely chopped
1 baking potato, peeled
½ teaspoon chili powder
¼ teaspoon ground cumin
¼ teaspoon paprika
⅛ teaspoon ground red pepper
2 tablespoons thinly sliced onion

1. Preheat oven to 350°F. Spray baking sheet with nonstick cooking spray. Combine oil and garlic in small bowl; let stand 15 minutes.

2. Place 1 quart water in medium saucepan; bring to a boil over high heat. Add potato; boil 12 minutes. Drain; let stand 10 minutes or until cool enough to handle. Meanwhile, combine chili powder, cumin, paprika and pepper in small bowl until well blended.*

3. Cut potato into 20 slices. Place onion slices on baking sheet; arrange potato slices over onion. Brush potato slices with half of oil mixture. Sprinkle half of spice mixture over potato slices. Bake 40 minutes, turning once and brushing with remaining oil and spice mixture.

*Or combine ¼ teaspoon ground paprika, ¼ teaspoon dried oregano leaves, ¼ teaspoon dried thyme leaves, ¼ teaspoon dried sage leaves and ⅛ teaspoon ground red pepper in small bowl until well blended.

Makes 2 servings

Dietary Exchanges per Serving:
1½ Starch/Bread, 1 Fat

NUTRIENTS PER SERVING:

Calories	172
% calories from fat	30
Total Fat	6 g
Saturated Fat	<1 g
Cholesterol	0 mg
Sodium	15 mg
Carbohydrate	28 g
Dietary Fiber	<1 g
Protein	3 g
Calcium	15 mg
Iron	1 mg
Vitamin A	39 RE
Vitamin C	19 mg

Zucchini Cakes

3 teaspoons reduced calorie margarine, divided
2 tablespoons finely chopped red onion
1 zucchini
½ baking potato, peeled
¼ cup cholesterol free egg substitute
4½ teaspoons whole wheat bread crumbs
1 teaspoon finely chopped fresh dill
Pinch ground white pepper

1. Melt 1½ teaspoons margarine in large skillet over medium heat. Add onion; cook and stir 5 minutes or until onion is tender.

2. Shred zucchini and potato with shredding disk of food processor or with grater. Drain.

3. Combine onion, zucchini, potato, egg substitute, bread crumbs, dill and pepper in medium bowl until well blended.

4. Melt remaining 1½ teaspoons margarine in large skillet over medium heat. Drop 4 heaping ¼-cupfuls mixture into skillet; flatten with back of wooden spoon to form 3-inch circles. Cook 10 minutes or until golden brown, turning once.

Makes 2 servings

Dietary Exchanges per Serving:
1 Starch/Bread, ½ Vegetable, ½ Fat

NUTRIENTS PER SERVING:

Calories	111
% calories from fat	24
Total Fat	3 g
Saturated Fat	1 g
Cholesterol	0 mg
Sodium	123 mg
Carbohydrate	17 g
Dietary Fiber	1 g
Protein	5 g
Calcium	26 mg
Iron	1 mg
Vitamin A	239 RE
Vitamin C	14 mg

Tomato & Corn Casserole

1 can (14½ ounces) Italian-style stewed
    tomatoes, drained
¾ cup frozen whole kernel corn, thawed
1 egg, slightly beaten
1 egg white
1 tablespoon skim milk
2 teaspoons finely chopped red onion,
    divided
⅛ teaspoon ground nutmeg
⅓ cup whole wheat bread crumbs
1 teaspoon grated Parmesan cheese
¼ teaspoon dried thyme leaves
⅛ teaspoon dried basil leaves
⅛ teaspoon paprika
1 teaspoon reduced calorie margarine

1. Preheat oven to 350°F. Spray 2-cup casserole with nonstick cooking spray.

2. Combine tomatoes, corn, egg, egg white, milk, 1½ teaspoons onion and nutmeg in medium bowl until well blended. Spoon into prepared casserole. Bake 15 minutes.

3. Meanwhile, combine remaining ½ teaspoon onion, bread crumbs, cheese, thyme, basil and paprika in small bowl. Add margarine. Blend until mixture resembles coarse crumbs. Sprinkle bread crumb mixture over casserole. Bake 20 minutes or until casserole is set and bread crumbs are browned. *Makes 2 servings*

Dietary Exchanges per Serving:
1 Starch/Bread, ½ Lean Meat, 2½ Vegetable

NUTRIENTS PER SERVING:

Calories	179
% calories from fat	21
Total Fat	5 g
Saturated Fat	1 g
Cholesterol	107 mg
Sodium	501 mg
Carbohydrate	28 g
Dietary Fiber	3 g
Protein	10 g
Calcium	107 mg
Iron	2 mg
Vitamin A	224 RE
Vitamin C	22 mg

Red Beans & Rice

2 teaspoons reduced calorie margarine
¾ cup rinsed, drained canned kidney
    beans
¼ cup finely chopped red onion
4 tablespoons finely chopped green
    onions
3 tablespoons finely chopped fresh
    parsley, divided
1 tablespoon finely chopped celery
    leaves
1 clove garlic, finely chopped
⅛ teaspoon dried sage leaves
⅛ teaspoon dried thyme leaves
⅛ teaspoon ground black pepper
    Pinch ground red pepper
¾ cup hot, cooked white rice

1. Melt margarine in large nonstick saucepan over medium heat. Add beans, onions, 2 tablespoons parsley, celery leaves, garlic, sage, thyme and peppers. Cook and stir 5 minutes or until vegetables are tender.

2. Serve bean mixture over hot, cooked rice. Sprinkle remaining 1 tablespoon parsley evenly over each serving.

Makes 2 servings

Dietary Exchanges per Serving:
2½ Starch/Bread, ½ Vegetable, ½ Fat

NUTRIENTS PER SERVING:

Calories	223
% calories from fat	10
Total Fat	3 g
Saturated Fat	<1 g
Cholesterol	0 mg
Sodium	51 mg
Carbohydrate	42 g
Dietary Fiber	2 g
Protein	9 g
Calcium	50 mg
Iron	4 mg
Vitamin A	123 RE
Vitamin C	15 mg

Green Pea & Rice Almondine

2 teaspoons reduced calorie margarine
1 cup frozen baby green peas
¼ teaspoon ground cardamom
¼ teaspoon ground cinnamon
  Pinch ground cloves
  Pinch ground white pepper
¾ cup cooked white rice
2 teaspoons slivered almonds

Melt margarine in medium nonstick skillet over medium heat. Add peas, cardamom, cinnamon, cloves and pepper. Cook and stir 10 minutes or until peas are tender. Add rice. Cook until heated through, stirring occasionally. Sprinkle almonds evenly over each serving.   *Makes 4 servings*

Dietary Exchanges per Serving:
1 Starch/Bread, ½ Fat

NUTRIENTS PER SERVING:

Calories	100
% calories from fat	16
Total Fat	2 g
Saturated Fat	<1 g
Cholesterol	0 mg
Sodium	57 mg
Carbohydrate	18 g
Dietary Fiber	2 g
Protein	3 g
Calcium	19 mg
Iron	1 mg
Vitamin A	48 RE
Vitamin C	4 mg

Mixed Vegetables with Couscous

¼ cup uncooked quick-cooking couscous
⅔ cup cubed peeled potato
2 teaspoons vegetable oil
1 clove garlic, finely chopped
⅔ cup thinly sliced zucchini
½ cup coarsely chopped red or green bell pepper
¼ cup plus 1 tablespoon finely chopped fresh parsley, divided
¼ cup finely chopped red onion
2 tablespoons finely chopped green onion
1 medium tomato, peeled, seeded, coarsely chopped
2 teaspoons finely chopped fresh dill
¼ cup prepared salsa

1. Prepare couscous according to package directions, omitting salt.

2. Place 1 cup water in small saucepan; bring to a boil over high heat. Add potato cubes. Boil 5 minutes or until potato cubes are tender. Drain.

3. Heat oil in large nonstick skillet over medium heat until hot. Add garlic. Cook and stir 1 minute. Add zucchini, pepper, ¼ cup parsley and onions. Cook and stir 3 minutes. Add potato, tomato, 2 tablespoons water and dill. Cook and stir 5 minutes or until water evaporates.

4. Combine couscous, vegetables and salsa in medium serving bowl. Sprinkle remaining 1 tablespoon parsley evenly over each serving. Garnish as desired

Makes 2 Servings

Dietary Exchanges per Serving:
2½ Starch/Bread, 1 Vegetable, 1 Fat

NUTRIENTS PER SERVING:

Calories	248
% calories from fat	19
Total Fat	5 g
Saturated Fat	<1 g
Cholesterol	0 mg
Sodium	28 mg
Carbohydrate	45 g
Dietary Fiber	8 g
Protein	7 g
Calcium	51 mg
Iron	2 mg
Vitamin A	391 RE
Vitamin C	97 mg

Green Pea & Rice Almondine

Spaghetti Squash Primavera

Spaghetti Squash Primavera

2 teaspoons vegetable oil
½ teaspoon finely chopped garlic
¼ cup finely chopped red onion
¼ cup thinly sliced carrot
¼ cup thinly sliced red bell pepper
¼ cup thinly sliced green bell pepper
1 can (14½ ounces) Italian-style stewed
    tomatoes, undrained
½ cup thinly sliced yellow squash
½ cup thinly sliced zucchini
½ cup frozen whole kernel corn, thawed
½ teaspoon dried oregano leaves
⅛ teaspoon dried thyme leaves
1 spaghetti squash (about 2 pounds)
4 teaspoons grated Parmesan cheese
    (optional)
2 tablespoons minced fresh parsley

1. Heat oil in large skillet. Add garlic. Cook and stir 3 minutes. Add onion, carrot and peppers. Cook and stir 3 minutes. Add tomatoes, squash, zucchini, corn, oregano and thyme. Cook and stir 5 minutes.

2. Cut squash lengthwise in half. Remove seeds. Cover with plastic wrap. Microwave at

HIGH 9 minutes or until squash separates easily into strands when tested with fork.

3. Cut each squash half lengthwise in half; separate strands with fork. Spoon vegetables evenly over halves. Top each serving evenly with cheese, if desired and parsley before serving. *Makes 4 servings*

Dietary Exchanges per Serving:
1 Starch/Bread, 1 Vegetable, ½ Fat

NUTRIENTS PER SERVING:

Calories	101
% calories from fat	25
Total Fat	3 g
Saturated Fat	<1 g
Cholesterol	0 mg
Sodium	11 mg
Carbohydrate	18 g
Dietary Fiber	5 g
Protein	3 g
Calcium	70 mg
Iron	1 mg
Vitamin A	309 RE
Vitamin C	48 mg

Broccoli & Red Bell Pepper Timbales

2 teaspoons reduced calorie margarine
¼ cup finely chopped red bell pepper
3 tablespoons finely chopped red onion
⅓ cup cholesterol free egg substitute
3 tablespoons whole wheat bread crumbs
3 tablespoons nonfat sour cream
2 tablespoons evaporated skim milk
⅛ teaspoon salt
⅛ teaspoon ground nutmeg
  Pinch ground black pepper
1 cup cooked frozen chopped broccoli
3 tablespoons shredded reduced fat Cheddar cheese

1. Preheat oven to 350°F. Spray two 6-ounce custard cups with nonstick cooking spray; set aside.

2. Melt margarine in small saucepan over medium heat. Add bell pepper and onion. Cook and stir 3 minutes or until vegetables are crisp-tender.

3. In food processor or blender combine egg substitute, bread crumbs, sour cream, milk, salt, nutmeg and black pepper; process until well blended. Stir bread crumb mixture, broccoli and cheese into saucepan; blend well.

4. Spoon broccoli mixture evenly into prepared custard cups; pack down with back of spoon. Bake 20 minutes or until mixture is set. Serve in custard cups.

Makes 2 servings

Dietary Exchanges per Serving:
1 Lean Meat, 3 Vegetable

NUTRIENTS PER SERVING:

Calories	139
% calories from fat	22
Total Fat	4 g
Saturated Fat	1 g
Cholesterol	6 mg
Sodium	441 mg
Carbohydrate	16 g
Dietary Fiber	5 g
Protein	12 g
Calcium	225 mg
Iron	2 mg
Vitamin A	714 RE
Vitamin C	102 mg

Apple-Filled Sweet Potatoes

2 small sweet potatoes or yams
1 Golden Delicious apple, peeled, cored, chopped
5 tablespoons frozen apple juice concentrate, thawed
½ teaspoon ground cinnamon
⅛ teaspoon ground nutmeg

1. Preheat oven to 400°F.

2. Pierce potatoes with fork. Bake 1 hour or until tender. Remove from oven; let stand 10 minutes or until cool enough to handle. Cut potatoes lengthwise in half. Scoop out pulp leaving ¼-inch-thick shells; reserve pulp.

3. Place apple in microwaveable dish; cover with plastic wrap. Microwave at HIGH 90 seconds. Let stand 10 minutes.

4. Preheat broiler. Combine reserved potato pulp, apple juice concentrate, cinnamon and nutmeg in small bowl until well blended. Add apple; toss to coat. Stuff potato halves evenly with apple mixture. Place halves on baking sheet. Broil 5 minutes or until tops are lightly browned.

Makes 4 servings

Dietary Exchanges per Serving:
1½ Starch/Bread, ½ Fruit

NUTRIENTS PER SERVING:

Calories	139
% calories from fat	2
Total Fat	<1 g
Saturated Fat	<1 g
Cholesterol	0 mg
Sodium	12 mg
Carbohydrate	34 g
Dietary Fiber	4 g
Protein	2 g
Calcium	34 mg
Iron	1 mg
Vitamin A	2,171 RE
Vitamin C	36 mg

Brown Rice & Mushrooms

Nonstick cooking spray
1 cup sliced mushrooms
1 tablespoon reduced calorie margarine
¼ cup finely chopped fresh parsley
3 tablespoons finely chopped green onions
½ cup frozen Italian broad beans, cooked, drained
¼ cup canned water chestnuts, rinsed, drained, thinly sliced
⅔ cup cooked brown rice

1. Spray large nonstick skillet with cooking spray; heat over medium heat until hot. Add mushrooms; cook and stir 5 minutes or until browned and tender. Remove mushrooms from skillet.

2. Melt margarine in same skillet over medium heat. Add parsley and green onions. Cook and stir 2 minutes or until onions are crisp-tender. Add mushrooms, beans, water chestnuts and rice. Cook until heated through, stirring occasionally. Serve immediately. *Makes 4 servings*

Dietary Exchanges per Serving:
1 Starch/Bread, ½ Vegetable, ½ Fat

NUTRIENTS PER SERVING:

Calories	100
% calories from fat	18
Total Fat	2 g
Saturated Fat	<1 g
Cholesterol	0 mg
Sodium	38 mg
Carbohydrate	18 g
Dietary Fiber	1 g
Protein	3 g
Calcium	20 mg
Iron	1 mg
Vitamin A	71 RE
Vitamin C	7 mg

Spinach Noodle Casserole

1 tablespoon reduced calorie margarine
¼ cup finely chopped red onion
¼ cup frozen chopped spinach, thawed
⅛ teaspoon ground nutmeg
2 pinches dried thyme leaves, divided
2 pinches ground white pepper, divided
⅔ cup 1% low fat cottage cheese
¼ cup nonfat sour cream
½ cup uncooked wide no-yolk noodles, cooked
⅓ cup whole wheat bread crumbs
2 teaspoons grated Parmesan cheese

1. Preheat oven to 375°F. Spray 2-cup casserole with nonstick cooking spray; set aside.

2. Melt margarine in small nonstick skillet over medium heat. Add onion. Cook and stir 2 minutes. Stir in spinach, nutmeg, 1 pinch thyme and 1 pinch pepper. Cook and stir 3 minutes or until onion is tender.

3. Combine cottage cheese and sour cream in medium bowl. Add spinach mixture and noodles; toss to combine. Spoon into prepared casserole.

4. Combine remaining pinch thyme, remaining pinch pepper, bread crumbs and Parmesan cheese in small bowl until well blended. Sprinkle bread crumb mixture evenly over casserole. Bake 30 minutes or until heated through. *Makes 2 servings*

Dietary Exchanges per Serving:
1½ Starch/Bread, 1½ Lean Meat, ½ Vegetable

NUTRIENTS PER SERVING:

Calories	201
% calories from fat	20
Total Fat	5 g
Saturated Fat	1 g
Cholesterol	5 mg
Sodium	544 mg
Carbohydrate	25 g
Dietary Fiber	2 g
Protein	17 g
Calcium	165 mg
Iron	1 mg
Vitamin A	403 RE
Vitamin C	4 mg

Broccoli & Cauliflower Stir-Fry

Broccoli & Cauliflower Stir-Fry

    2 dry-pack sun-dried tomatoes
    4 teaspoons reduced sodium soy
      sauce
    1 tablespoon rice wine vinegar
    1 teaspoon brown sugar
    1 teaspoon Oriental sesame oil
    ⅛ teaspoon crushed red pepper
  2¼ teaspoons vegetable oil
    2 cups cauliflowerets
    2 cups broccoli flowerets
    1 clove garlic, finely chopped
    ⅓ cup thinly sliced red or green bell
      pepper

1. Place tomatoes in small bowl; cover with boiling water. Let stand 5 minutes. Drain; coarsely chop. Meanwhile, combine soy sauce, vinegar, sugar, sesame oil and red pepper in small bowl until well blended.

2. Heat vegetable oil in wok or large nonstick skillet until hot. Add califlower, broccoli and garlic; stir-fry 4 minutes. Add tomatoes and pepper; stir-fry 1 minute or

until vegetables are crisp-tender. Add soy sauce mixture; cook and stir until heated through. Serve immediately.

Makes 2 servings

Dietary Exchanges per Serving:
6 Vegetable, 1½ Fat

NUTRIENTS PER SERVING:

Calories	214
% calories from fat	30
Total Fat	8 g
Saturated Fat	1 g
Cholesterol	0 mg
Sodium	443 mg
Carbohydrate	32 g
Dietary Fiber	5 g
Protein	9 g
Calcium	115 mg
Iron	3 mg
Vitamin A	1,493 RE
Vitamin C	249 mg

Guilt-Free Desserts

Tickle your taste buds with this dazzling array of luscious, yet lean desserts. Cheesecakes, brownies and cakes have never been so sweet—and so healthy.

Chocolate-Berry Cheesecake

1 cup chocolate wafer crumbs
1 container (12 ounces) fat free cream cheese
1 package (8 ounces) reduced fat cream cheese
⅔ cup sugar
½ cup cholesterol free egg substitute
3 tablespoons skim milk
1¼ teaspoons vanilla
1 cup mini semisweet chocolate chips
2 tablespoons raspberry all fruit spread
2½ cups fresh strawberries, stems removed, halved

1. Preheat oven to 350°F. Spray bottom of 9-inch springform pan with nonstick cooking spray.

2. Press chocolate wafer crumbs firmly onto side or bottom of prepared pan. Bake 10 minutes. Remove from oven; cool. *Reduce oven temperature to 325°F.*

3. Combine cheeses in large bowl with electric mixer. Beat at medium speed until well blended. Beat in sugar until well blended. Beat in egg substitute, milk and vanilla until well blended. Stir in mini chips with spoon. Pour batter into prepared pan.

4. Bake 40 minutes or until center is set. Remove from oven; cool 10 minutes in pan on wire rack. Carefully loosen cheesecake from edge of pan. Cool completely.

5. Remove side of pan from cake. Whisk fruit spread and 2 tablespoons water in medium bowl until well blended. Add strawberries; toss to coat. Arrange strawberries over top of cake. Refrigerate 1 hour before serving. Garnish with fresh mint, if desired. *Makes 16 servings*

Dietary Exchanges per Serving:
1 Starch/Bread, ½ Lean Meat, 1 Fruit, 1 Fat

NUTRIENTS PER SERVING:

Calories	197
% calories from fat	29
Total Fat	7 g
Saturated Fat	2 g
Cholesterol	7 mg
Sodium	290 mg
Carbohydrate	29 g
Dietary Fiber	<1 g
Protein	7 g
Calcium	205 mg
Iron	1 mg
Vitamin A	172 RE
Vitamin C	13 mg

Cheese-Filled Poached Pear

Cheese-Filled Poached Pears

1½ quarts cran-raspberry juice cocktail
2 ripe Bartlett pears with stems, peeled
2 tablespoons Neufchâtel cheese
2 teaspoons crumbled Gorgonzola
   cheese
1 tablespoon ground walnuts

1. Bring juice to a boil in medium saucepan over high heat. Add pears; reduce heat to medium-low. Simmer 15 minutes or until pears are tender, turning occasionally. Remove pears from saucepan; discard liquid. Let stand 10 minutes or until cool enough to handle.

2. Combine cheeses in small bowl until well blended. Cut thin slice off bottom of each pear so that pear will stand evenly. Cut pears lengthwise in half leaving stem attached to one half of each pear. Scoop out seeds and membranes to form small hole in each pear half.

3. Spoon cheese mixture evenly into each pear half; press halves together. Place nuts in large bowl; roll pears in nuts to coat. Cover; refrigerate until ready to serve.
Makes 2 servings

Dietary Exchanges per Serving:
½ Lean Meat, 3 Fruit, 1 Fat

NUTRIENTS PER SERVING:

Calories	240
% calories from fat	24
Total Fat	7 g
Saturated Fat	3 g
Cholesterol	13 mg
Sodium	98 mg
Carbohydrate	45 g
Dietary Fiber	4 g
Protein	4 g
Calcium	53 mg
Iron	1 mg
Vitamin A	58 RE
Vitamin C	41 mg

Oatmeal Raisin Drops

1 cup all-purpose flour
1 cup uncooked rolled oats
1 teaspoon baking powder
1 teaspoon ground cinnamon
½ teaspoon ground nutmeg
½ teaspoon baking soda
⅛ teaspoon ground cloves
¾ cup frozen apple juice concentrate, thawed
3 tablespoons cholesterol free egg substitute
2 tablespoons margarine, melted
2 teaspoons vanilla
½ cup raisins

1. Preheat oven to 375°F. Spray baking sheets with nonstick cooking spray.

2. Combine flour, oats, baking powder, cinnamon, nutmeg, baking soda and cloves in large bowl. Combine remaining ingredients in medium bowl; blend well. Add to dry ingredients; blend well. Cover; refrigerate 20 minutes.

3. Drop tablespoonfuls dough 2 inches apart onto prepared baking sheets. Bake 20 minutes or until lightly browned. Cool completely on wire racks.

Makes 28 cookies

Dietary Exchanges per Serving:
½ Starch/Bread, 1 Fruit

NUTRIENTS PER SERVING:
2 cookies

Calories	100
% calories from fat	17
Total Fat	2 g
Saturated Fat	<1 g
Cholesterol	0 mg
Sodium	85 mg
Carbohydrate	19 g
Dietary Fiber	1 g
Protein	2 g
Calcium	16 mg
Iron	1 mg
Vitamin A	33 RE
Vitamin C	18 mg

Apple Raspberry Tart

1¼ cups all-purpose flour
¼ teaspoon baking powder
Dash salt
¼ cup vegetable oil
3 tablespoons skim milk
⅓ cup frozen apple juice concentrate, thawed
3 tablespoons cornstarch
¾ teaspoon ground cinnamon
⅛ teaspoon ground nutmeg
4 heaping cups thinly sliced peeled Golden Delicious apples
2 cups fresh or thawed frozen raspberries
¼ cup packed brown sugar

1. Preheat oven to 350°F. Combine flour, baking powder and salt in medium bowl. Stir in oil and milk until well blended. Shape dough into a ball.

2. Place dough on lightly floured surface. Roll out dough into 10-inch circle, ⅛ inch thick. Ease into 9-inch pie plate. Trim edge.

3. Whisk apple juice concentrate, cornstarch, cinnamon and nutmeg in large bowl until well blended. Add fruit; toss to coat. Spoon fruit mixture into prepared pie crust; sprinkle sugar evenly over top of fruit.

4. Bake 50 minutes or until crust is golden brown. Let stand 30 minutes before serving.

Makes 8 servings

Dietary Exchanges per Serving:
1½ Starch/Bread, 1 Fruit, 1½ Fat

NUTRIENTS PER SERVING:
Calories	243
% calories from fat	27
Total Fat	7 g
Saturated Fat	1 g
Cholesterol	<1 mg
Sodium	19 mg
Carbohydrate	43 g
Dietary Fiber	3 g
Protein	3 g
Calcium	32 mg
Iron	1 mg
Vitamin A	10 RE
Vitamin C	26 mg

Apricot Cocoa Squares

1 cup granulated sugar
5 tablespoons margarine, softened
2 jars (2½ ounces each) first stage
   baby food prunes
½ cup cholesterol free egg substitute
⅓ cup skim milk
1¾ teaspoons vanilla
1½ cups all-purpose flour
⅓ cup unsweetened cocoa
1 teaspoon baking powder
1 cup coarsely chopped dried apricots
2 teaspoons powdered sugar (optional)

1. Preheat oven to 350°F. Spray 13 × 9-inch baking pan with nonstick cooking spray.

2. Combine granulated sugar and margarine in large bowl with electric mixer. Beat at medium speed until light and fluffy. Beat in prunes until well blended.

3. Combine egg substitute, milk and vanilla in small bowl. Sift flour, cocoa and baking powder into another small bowl. Add flour mixture alternately with egg mixture to sugar mixture; beat at medium speed until well blended. Stir in apricots with spoon. Spoon batter into prepared pan.

4. Bake 30 minutes or until wooden pick inserted in center comes out clean. Cool completely in pan. Cut into squares. Dust with powdered sugar before serving.

Makes 28 squares

Dietary Exchanges per Serving:
1½ Starch/Bread, ½ Fruit, 1 Fat

NUTRIENTS PER SERVING:
2 squares

Calories	180
% calories from fat	21
Total Fat	4 g
Saturated Fat	1 g
Cholesterol	<1 mg
Sodium	89 mg
Carbohydrate	34 g
Dietary Fiber	1 g
Protein	3 g
Calcium	26 mg
Iron	2 mg
Vitamin A	167 RE
Vitamin C	1 mg

Pumpkin Pie

6 tablespoons reduced calorie
   margarine
1¼ cups graham cracker crumbs
1 can (16 ounces) solid pack pumpkin
1 can (12 ounces) evaporated skim milk
½ cup packed brown sugar
1 egg
2 egg whites
1 teaspoon ground cinnamon
1 teaspoon vanilla
½ teaspoon ground ginger
¼ teaspoon ground nutmeg
⅛ teaspoon ground cloves

1. Preheat oven to 350°F. Melt margarine in small saucepan over medium heat. Stir in graham cracker crumbs until well blended. Press mixture firmly onto bottom and up side of 9-inch pie plate. Bake 10 minutes.

2. Combine remaining ingredients in large bowl until well blended. Pour into prepared pie crust.

3. Bake 30 to 40 minutes or until knife inserted in center comes out clean. Cool completely in pan on wire rack before serving. *Makes 12 servings*

Dietary Exchanges per Serving:
1 Starch/Bread, ½ Milk, 1 Fat

NUTRIENTS PER SERVING:

Calories	163
% calories from fat	27
Total Fat	5 g
Saturated Fat	1 g
Cholesterol	19 mg
Sodium	188 mg
Carbohydrate	25 g
Dietary Fiber	1 g
Protein	5 g
Calcium	117 mg
Iron	1 mg
Vitamin A	944 RE
Vitamin C	2 mg

Streusel-Topped Baked Apples

⅓ cup whole wheat bread crumbs
2 teaspoons brown sugar
5 teaspoons finely chopped walnuts, divided
¼ teaspoon ground cinnamon
1½ teaspoons reduced calorie margarine
2 Jonathan apples
¼ cup plus 3 tablespoons frozen apple juice concentrate, thawed, divided

1. Preheat oven to 375°F. Combine bread crumbs, sugar, 3 teaspoons walnuts and cinnamon in small bowl. Cut in margarine with pastry blender until mixture resembles coarse crumbs.

2. Core apples to within ½ inch of bottoms. Peel top halves of apples. Cut thin slice from top of each apple to form edge.

3. Spoon remaining walnuts and 1½ teaspoons apple juice concentrate into each apple. Place apples in small baking dish. Pour remaining apple juice concentrate and 2 tablespoons water into baking dish.

4. Bake 35 minutes, brushing occasionally with cooking liquid. Spoon bread crumb mixture evenly into and onto top edges of apples.

5. Bake 20 minutes or until apples are just tender. Pour cooking liquid over apples before serving.　　*Makes 2 servings*

Dietary Exchanges per Serving:
½ Starch/Bread, 3½ Fruit, 1 Fat

NUTRIENTS PER SERVING:

Calories	278
% calories from fat	18
Total Fat	6 g
Saturated Fat	1 g
Cholesterol	0 mg
Sodium	109 mg
Carbohydrate	57 g
Dietary Fiber	3 g
Protein	3 g
Calcium	43 mg
Iron	2 mg
Vitamin A	42 RE
Vitamin C	91 mg

No-Guilt Chocolate Brownies

1 cup semisweet chocolate chips
¼ cup packed brown sugar
2 tablespoons granulated sugar
½ teaspoon baking powder
¼ teaspoon salt
½ cup cholesterol free egg substitute
1 jar (2½ ounces) first stage baby food prunes
1 teaspoon vanilla
1 cup uncooked rolled oats
⅓ cup nonfat dry milk solids
¼ cup wheat germ
2 teaspoons powdered sugar

1. Preheat oven to 350°F. Spray 8 × 8-inch square baking pan with nonstick cooking spray; set aside. Melt chips in top of double boiler over simmering water.

2. Combine brown and granulated sugars, baking powder and salt in large bowl with electric mixer. Add egg substitute, prunes and vanilla. Beat at medium speed until well blended. Stir in oats, milk solids, wheat germ and chocolate.

3. Pour batter into pan. Bake 30 minutes or until wooden pick inserted in center comes out clean. Cool completely. Cut into squares. Dust with powdered sugar before serving.
Makes 16 servings

Dietary Exchanges per Serving:
1 Starch/Bread, 1 Fat

NUTRIENTS PER SERVING:

Calories	124
% calories from fat	30
Total Fat	5 g
Saturated Fat	<1 g
Cholesterol	<1 mg
Sodium	65 mg
Carbohydrate	21 g
Dietary Fiber	<1 g
Protein	3 g
Calcium	33 mg
Iron	1 mg
Vitamin A	53 RE
Vitamin C	<1 mg

Peach & Blackberry Shortcakes

¾ cup plain low fat yogurt, divided
5 teaspoons sugar, divided
1 tablespoon blackberry all fruit spread
½ cup coarsely chopped peeled peach
½ cup fresh or thawed frozen blackberries or raspberries
½ cup all-purpose flour
¼ teaspoon baking powder
⅛ teaspoon baking soda
2 tablespoons reduced calorie margarine
½ teaspoon vanilla

1. Place cheesecloth or coffee filter in large sieve or strainer. Spoon yogurt into sieve; place over large bowl. Refrigerate 20 minutes. Remove yogurt from sieve; discard liquid. Measure ¼ cup yogurt; reserve. Combine remaining yogurt, 2 teaspoons sugar and fruit spread in small bowl until well blended; refrigerate until ready to serve.

2. Meanwhile, combine peach, blackberries and ½ teaspoon sugar in medium bowl; set aside.

3. Preheat oven to 425°F.

4. Combine flour, baking powder, baking soda and remaining 2½ teaspoons sugar in small bowl. Cut in margarine with pastry blender or two knives until mixture resembles coarse crumbs. Combine reserved ¼ cup yogurt with vanilla. Stir into flour mixture just until dry ingredients are moistened. Shape dough into a ball.

5. Place dough on lightly floured surface. Knead dough gently 8 times. Divide dough in half. Roll out each half with lightly floured rolling pin into 3-inch circle. Place circles onto ungreased baking sheet.

6. Bake 12 to 15 minutes or until lightly browned. Immediately remove from baking sheet. Cool shortcakes on wire rack 10 minutes or until cool enough to handle.

7. Cut each shortcake in half. Spoon fruit mixture evenly over bottom halves. Spoon yogurt mixture evenly over fruit; top with remaining shortcake halves. Garnish with blackberries and mint, if desired. Serve immediately. *Makes 2 servings*

Dietary Exchanges per Serving:
2½ Starch/Bread, ½ Milk, 1 Fruit, 1 Fat

NUTRIENTS PER SERVING:

Calories	327
% calories from fat	21
Total Fat	8 g
Saturated Fat	2 g
Cholesterol	5 mg
Sodium	311 mg
Carbohydrate	57 g
Dietary Fiber	4 g
Protein	8 g
Calcium	183 mg
Iron	2 mg
Vitamin A	176 RE
Vitamin C	11 mg

Health Note: Most fruits, vegetables and whole grains are high in fiber and in the antioxidants, vitamins C and E, and beta-carotene. These nutrients work to neutralize substances such as smog and cigarette smoke that have damaging effects on our cells.

Peach & Blackberry Shortcake